A Guide to Patient Satisfaction Survey Instruments

Profiles of Patient Satisfaction Measurement
Instruments and Their Use by Health Plans,
Employers, Hospitals, and Insurers

Atlantic Information Services, Inc.
1100 17th Street, NW, Suite 300 • Washington, D.C. 20036 • (202) 775-9008 • www.aispub.com

Other Health Care Management Books Available from AIS

Effective Fraud Control Tactics for Insurers and Managed Care Plans

Planning and Implementing Your Health Care Internet Strategy

Implementing a Successful Medicare Managed Care Product

Health Care Report Cards

A Guide to Buying Physician Practices

Navigating Your Way Through the Federal Physician Self-Referral Law

Designing a Health Care Corporate Compliance Program

Managed Care Facts, Trends and Data

Managed Medicare & Medicaid Facts, Trends and Data

Call 1-800-521-4323 for further information.

ISBN: 0-929156-11-0

Visit the Atlantic Information Services "Health Care Info-Station" at www.aispub.com on the World Wide Web.

For reprint permission, or information regarding individual or bulk purchases, contact Atlantic Information Services, Inc., 1100 17th Street, NW, Suite 300, Washington, D.C. 20036 (1-800-521-4323; 202-775-9008).

Table of Contents

Table of Contents (continued)

Foreword

Hospitals, health plans and medical practices increasingly are using the results of patient satisfaction surveys to identify problems, re-engineer their clinical and customer services, incentivize physician behavior, and attract and retain customers. Employers are also using these surveys to help them and their employees compare competing plans and make educated purchasing decisions.

Patient satisfaction surveys will continue to grow in importance as more and more consumers begin to seek information on which to base their own health care purchasing choices. And as capitation and other contracting arrangements narrow the price gaps between providers, superior customer satisfaction is key to survival.

This publication shows you how providers are using surveys to gather valuable data on customer satisfaction. It also includes information on instruments developed by several national consulting companies and sold or licensed to providers.

Sample pages are included for as many survey instruments as possible. Many instruments, however, are proprietary and sample pages could not be reprinted. Contact information has been provided for each survey profiled.

Your comments, suggestions and, especially, news of patient satisfaction survey instruments *not* included this edition would be greatly appreciated. Please address them to Steve Goodwin at AIS.

Overview

"Patient Satisfaction" Can Mean a Lot of Different Things

by Diane Glancey, M.A. and Liz Dunn, Ph.D.

Patient satisfaction scores have become increasingly important in the health care market place. Hospitals want to show good patient satisfaction scores to managed care organizations during the bargaining process. Managed care organizations want to show good member hospital satisfaction scores to employers when they are negotiating contracts. In some cases, physicians who get low scores from their patients may receive lower compensation from their managed care contractors.

Despite the acknowledged importance of patient satisfaction scores, there is an unacceptable amount of variability among the questionnaires that are used to collect these data. While some questionnaires have been subjected to rigorous tests of reliability and validity, others are little more than home-made instruments.

One of the major differences among these questionnaires is the validity of questions that are asked of the patient. There are two basic approaches to deciding which questions should be asked of patients. The first approach is simply to ask the patients. When you are designing or updating a patient questionnaire, it is essential to get patient input into the process. This can be accomplished by inviting a group of recently discharged patients and their significant others to an informal focus group, and asking them what questions they think should be included in a patient satisfaction questionnaire.

While patients may not give you questions in the exact format that you need them, they definitely are more qualified to determine the content of most questions than anyone else.

A second approach to evaluating which questions to use is to perform a correlation analysis on data that you have already collected. The idea is to measure the "imputed importance" of a particular questions by correlating it with some "bottom line" question. For example, you might correlate the question "How satisfied were you with your meals?" with the following "bottom line question:" "Overall, how satisfied were you with your hospital experience?" If the resulting correlation coefficient is relatively low, we know that the question is not that important to overall satisfaction, and we may wish to omit it from subsequent surveys.

At Thomas Jefferson University hospital, we measure the correlation between every question and our "bottom line question:" "Overall, how do you rate the quality of the care you received in our hospital?" We have found that the following questions show the following correlations:

	Correlation with perceived quality
Satisfaction with nursing	.89
Satisfaction with physicians	.87
Satisfaction with discharge process	.79
Satisfaction with room	.79

While these relationships may seem obvious, others do not. In our last study, we obtained the following results:

	Correlation with perceived quality
Overall, would you say your health is much better, somewhat better, about the same, somewhat worse, or much worse at this point following your hospital stay?	**.49**
What is your level of agreement with the statement: "The hospital staff tried to reduce your stress level?"	**.85**

The results show that perceptions of whether the hospital staff tried to reduce anxiety is more strongly related to overall satisfaction than perceptions of how much health status improved. This is consistent with the results of our previous qualitative research. Because of the very strong relationship between perceived anxiety reduction and overall satisfaction, we recommend that any new or revised questionnaires include such a question.

In summary, not every patient satisfaction questionnaire includes questions that are valid (relevant to patient satisfaction). Two ways to ensure that questions are relevant are (1) include patient input into the questions and (2) perform a correlation analysis between each question and some "bottom line question."

This article appeared at pages 5-6 of the May 1996 issue of Health Policy Newsletter, *which is published by the Office of Health Policy and Clinical Outcomes at the Thomas Jefferson University Hospital/Jefferson Medical College. It is reprinted here with their permission. For further information, contact Elizabeth L. Brown, TJUH/JMC, 1015 Walnut Street, Suite 621, Philadelphia, Penn. 19107,*

American Managed Behavioral Healthcare Association

Washington, D.C.

Title of Survey: PERMS 1.0, Performance Measures for Managed Behavioral Healthcare Programs

Profile of Organization: The American Managed Behavioral Healthcare Association (AMBHA) is a trade association of managed behavioral health firms.

Date Survey was Created: September 1995.

Overview of Survey: N/A

Survey Used to Measure Patient Satisfaction With:

- Quality of medical care received from health plans, hospitals and other providers;
- Customer services;
- Costs of care;
- Access to care;
- Coverage.

Type of Patient Completing Survey: Health plan enrollees who have used a service.

When do Patients/Enrollees Complete Survey?: Two to six months after intake.

Background Information Collected on Those Completing the Survey: None.

How are Survey Findings Used?: Data will be collected by Harvard University and the results will be released on October 8, 1996, at the National Stakeholders Conference.

Date of Last Revision to Survey: N/A

Purchase Price of Survey: $25.

Contact Information: E. Clarke Ross, D.P.A., American Managed Behavioral Healthcare Association, 700 Thirteenth Street, NW, Suite 950, Washington, D.C. 20001, (202) 434-4565; fax (202) 434-4564.

Bon Secours Health System, Inc.

Marriottsville, Md.

Title of Survey: NCG Research's "Your Hospital Stay: The Patient's Viewpoint" (See **NCG Research** entry on Page 59.)

Profile of Organization: Bon Secours Health System, headquartered in Marriottsville, Md., includes seven owned hospitals with just under 2,000 beds in five states.

Date Survey was Created: 1990.

Overview of Survey: Survey consists of 11 questions seeking general information; 40 questions rating service attributes on a "poor" to "excellent" scale; three questions on customer loyalty; three open-ended questions on needed improvements and things done well; seven demographic questions.

Survey Used to Measure Patient Satisfaction With:

- Quality of medical care received from doctors and hospitals;
- Customer services;
- Costs of care;
- Outcomes.

Type of Patient Completing Survey: Random sample of patients each month.

When do Patients/Enrollees Complete Survey?: Fifteen to 45 days after discharge.

Background Information Collected on Those Completing the Survey: Demographic.

How are Survey Findings Used?: To identify opportunities for process improvement, track the results of improvement efforts and serve as an early warning system for processes needing attention.

Date of Last Revision to Survey: 1994.

Purchase Price of Survey: See **NCG Research** entry on Page 59.

Contact Information: Ross Brady, Bon Secours Health System, Inc., 1505 Marriottsville Road, Marriottsville, Md. 21104, (410) 442-3202; fax (410) 442-1082; e-mail ross_brady@bshsi.com

California Public Employees' Retirement System

Sacramento, Calif.

Title of Survey: Health Plan Experience Survey

Profile of Organization: California Public Employees' Retirement System (CalPERS) provides health benefits to nearly 1 million California employees, retirees, and their families from nearly 1,000 state and local public agencies. It is the second largest health insurance risk pool in the nation.

Date Survey was Created: 1991.

Overview of Survey: Survey collects confidential data on employees' personal experience with their health plans. Members are asked if their health plan representatives were helpful, if they've had past administrative problems, if they regularly receive educational materials, and whether or not they are satisfied with their choice of doctors.

Survey Used to Measure Patient Satisfaction With:

- Prescription drug plans;
- Quality of medical care received from doctors;
- Access to care;
- Time spent waiting to receive services;
- Survey also asks how members feel about services outside of their geographic area.

Type of Patient Completing Survey: Enrollees.

When do Patients/Enrollees Complete Survey?: N/A

Background Information Collected on Those Completing the Survey: Demographic.

How are Survey Findings Used?: N/A

Date of Last Revision to Survey: N/A

Purchase Price of Survey: N/A

Contact Information: California Public Employees' Retirement System, Health Plan Administration Division, P.O. Box 720724, Sacramento, Calif. 94229-0724, (916) 326-3358; fax (916) 558-4105.

CareData Reports, Inc.

New York, N.Y.

Title of Survey: CareData Annual Survey of Health Plan Member Satisfaction

Profile of Organization: CareData Reports, Inc. is a health care research company that provides comparative consumer information on managed care plans. The privately-held company is affiliated with The Wilkerson Group and Data Development Corp.

Date Survey was Created: N/A

Overview of Survey: Survey, which divulges top-performing plans, studies such areas as:

- Adequacy of medical care, including care during pregnancy, high blood pressure treatment, asthma care, diabetes care, cancer care, drug and alcohol rehabilitation, mental health care and smoking cessation.

- Satisfaction with aspects of health plans, including quality and reputation of hospitals, pharmacy benefits, specialists, primary care physicians, customer service, plan administration and concern shown for well-being.

The 1995 survey focused on five areas: Southern California, Houston, Connecticut, New Jersey and Greater Cleveland.

Survey Used to Measure Patient Satisfaction With: See above.

Type of Patient Completing Survey: Health plan enrollee.

When do Patients/Enrollees Complete Survey?: Annually.

Background Information Collected on Those Completing the Survey: N/A

How are Survey Findings Used?: To independently study the performance of managed care health plans relative to their regional competitors, as well as to collect market intelligence for health plans, health providers, benefits consultants, insurance brokers, analysts, and medical products manufacturers.

Date of Last Revision to Survey: 1995.

Purchase Price of Survey: N/A

Contact Information: CareData Reports, Inc., 666 Third Avenue, 23rd Floor, New York, N.Y. 10017-4036, (212) 883-4035; fax (212) 972-1821.

Center for the Study of Services

Washington, D.C.

Title of Survey: How Do You Rate Your Health Plan?

Profile of Organization: The Center For the Study of Services is a nonprofit company providing consumer information in service industries, including health care.

Date Survey was Created: N/A

Overview of Survey: Survey asks randomly selected employees to rate their health plan's performance over the past 12 months.

Survey Used to Measure Patient Satisfaction With:

- Quality of care received from doctors and other providers;
- Coverage;
- Available physicians;
- Customer services;
- Costs of care;
- Overall quality of care.

Type of Patient Completing Survey: Randomly selected employees.

When do Patients/Enrollees Complete Survey?: N/A

Background Information Collected on Those Completing the Survey: Demographic, including age, education and income.

How are Survey Findings Used?: To provide federal employees with patient satisfaction data on HMOs participating in the United States Office of Personnel Management's Federal Employees Health Benefits Program. Results are reported in *Washington Consumers' Checkbook* magazine.

Date of Last Revision to Survey: N/A

Purchase Price of Survey: Questionnaire is a copyrighted instrument. Licenses for its use are available from The Center for the Study of Services, in some cases at no cost.

Contact Information: The Center for the Study of Services, 733 15th Street, NW, Suite 820, Washington, D.C. 20005, (202) 347-7283; fax (202) 347-4000.

QUALITY OF CARE FROM DOCTORS AND OTHER MEDICAL PROFESSIONALS (including nurse practitioners, midwives, and physician's assistants) (circle a number to show your answer)	POOR	FAIR	GOOD	VERY GOOD	EXCELLENT	CAN'T RATE
11. Thoroughness, carefulness, and apparent competence of examinations and treatment	1	2	3	4	5	0
12. Follow-through on care—checking your progress, telling about test results, reminding you to seek follow-up care	1	2	3	4	5	0
13. How well the medical professionals work together to coordinate your care	1	2	3	4	5	0
14. Listening to you, including making you feel comfortable about asking questions and not interrupting you	1	2	3	4	5	0
15. Explanations of what is wrong, what is being done, and what you can expect	1	2	3	4	5	0
16. Getting you involved in making decisions about your care, including giving you the information needed to make informed choices	1	2	3	4	5	0
17. Courtesy and respect shown to you	1	2	3	4	5	0
18. Personal interest in you and your medical problems	1	2	3	4	5	0
19. Advice you are given about ways to stay healthy and avoid illness	1	2	3	4	5	0
20. Amount of time you have with the doctor or other medical professional during a visit	1	2	3	4	5	0
21. Results of care—how much you have been helped, how well your care has met your needs	1	2	3	4	5	0
22. *Overall rating for* quality of care	1	2	3	4	5	0

Chicago Business Group on Health
Chicago, Ill.

Title of Survey: Chicago Health Plan Value Project (CHPVP)

Profile of Organization: The Chicago Business Group on Health is an employer coalition and a chapter of the Midwest Business Group on Health.

Date Survey was Created: December 1995.

Overview of Survey: The survey covers issues of cost, quality, access and services of managed care plans. Survey is 24 pages in length, with 73 questions. Sponsors can customize survey to add questions about specifics in their benefit plans. Survey takes approximately 20 minutes to complete. Sections include: "Your 1994 Health Plan Choice," "Your Health Plan Overall," "Primary Care Physicians," "Specialty Care Physicians," "Emergency Care," "Hospital Facilities," "1994 Health Plan Administration," "1994 Experiences" and "Your Health Status."

Survey Used to Measure Patient Satisfaction With:

- Quality of medical care received from doctors, health plans, hospitals and doctors' office staff;
- Customer services;
- Access to care;
- Coverage;
- Self-reported health status of respondent.

Type of Patient Completing Survey: Random sample of all employees in a health plan and a random sample of a plan's commercial book of business.

When do Patients/Enrollees Complete Survey?: Annually.

Background Information Collected on Those Completing the Survey: Demographic.

How are Survey Findings Used?: For contract negotiations, performance guarantees, open enrollment information, user groups with plans and quality improvement activities.

Date of Last Revision to Survey: March 1, 1996.

Purchase Price of Survey: N/A

Contact Information: Larry Boress, Vice President, Chicago Business Group on Health, 8303 West Higgins Street, Suite 200, Chicago, Ill. 60631, (312) 380-9090; fax (312) 380-9096.

About 1994 Health Plan Administration

59. How satisfied were you with the overall quality of your Health Plan's Member Services in 1994 (for example, answering questions, resolving issues with coverage, etc.)? *(Circle one number)*

Very Dissatisfied	Dissatisfied	Somewhat Dissatisfied	Somewhat Satisfied	Satisfied	Very Satisfied
1	2	3	4	5	6

(19)

About Your 1994 Health Plan Experiences

60. Which of the following statements best describes your overall experience with your Health Plan in 1994? *(Circle one number)*

I did not have any problems .... 1 → **Skip to Question 62, Page 16** (20)

I had a few problems, but they were easily resolved .... 2 → **Continue to Question 61**

I had a few problems, and they were difficult to resolve .... 3 → **Continue to Question 61**

I had problems that were not resolved to my satisfaction 4 → **Continue to Question 61**

61. a. In Column 1, please circle each type of problem you experienced with your Health Plan in 1994. *(Circle all that apply)*

   b. In Column 2, please circle the **one** problem you experienced that you feel was the most significant problem. *(Circle one number)*

	Column 1	Column 2	
Referrals to specialists	1	1	(21-32)
Emergency care	2	2	(33-34)
Medical care while traveling or away from home	3	3	
Questions about covered services	4	4	
Policies concerning hospitalization	5	5	
Delays in your medical care while waiting for approval by your Health Plan	6	6	
Limits in your choice of doctors	7	7	
Limited freedom to receive the treatment plan you and your doctor believed was necessary	8	8	
Lack of information to help you manage or prevent medical problems	9	9	
Lack of reminders or encouragement to use timely preventive services	10	10	
Issues/problems with particular network physicians ...	11	11	
Other *(Please specify)*_____	12	12	

   c. Please describe in more detail the most significant problem you indicated in Column 2 above. *(Write in below)*

_____ (35-37)

_____ (38-40)

8

Children's Farm Home

Corvallis, Ore.

Title of Survey: Client Satisfaction Survey

Profile of Organization: Children's Farm Home is a residential treatment facility for emotionally-troubled youth.

Date Survey was Created: June 1995.

Overview of Survey: N/A

Survey Used to Measure Patient Satisfaction With:

- Quality of medical care received from doctors and other providers;
- Customer services;
- Various aspects of care, including recreation, therapy, dietary, nursing, milieu, safety, medical and case planning.

Type of Patient Completing Survey: All psychiatric residential treatment patients.

When do Patients/Enrollees Complete Survey?: At discharge and 90 days after discharge.

Background Information Collected on Those Completing the Survey: None.

How are Survey Findings Used?: To identify opportunities for improving delivery of psychiatric services.

Date of Last Revision to Survey: Scheduled to be revised in June 1996.

Purchase Price of Survey: N/A

Contact Information: Rich Blum, Children's Farm Home, 4455 NE Highway 20, Corvallis, Ore. 97330, (541) 757-1852; fax (541) 757-1944.

Children's Farm Home

Corvallis, Ore.

Title of Survey: Family Satisfaction Survey

Profile of Organization: Children's Farm Home is a residential treatment facility for emotionally-troubled youth.

Date Survey was Created: June 1995.

Overview of Survey: N/A

Survey Used to Measure Patient Satisfaction With:

- Quality of medical care received from doctors and other providers;
- Customer services;
- Various aspects of care, including nursing, milieu, therapies, dietary, vocational.

Type of Patient Completing Survey: Parents of children who are clients of psychiatric residential treatment.

When do Patients/Enrollees Complete Survey?: At discharge and 90 days post-discharge.

Background Information Collected on Those Completing the Survey: None.

How are Survey Findings Used?: To identify opportunities for improving delivery of psychiatric services.

Date of Last Revision to Survey: Scheduled to be revised in June 1996.

Purchase Price of Survey: N/A

Contact Information: Richard Blum, Children's Farm Home, 4455 NE Highway 20, Corvallis, Ore. 97330, (541) 757-1852; fax (541) 757-1944.

ChoiceCare

Cincinnati, Ohio

Title of Survey: PCP-Patient Satisfaction Measurement Program

Profile of Organization: ChoiceCare is a Cincinnati HMO with just over 255,000 enrollees. It contracts with and/or uses 19 area hospitals and over 2,800 physicians.

Date Survey was Created: March 1992.

Overview of Survey: Survey instrument is composed of 16 close-ended questions that evaluate the level of satisfaction members have with their primary care provider regarding service, quality and access to care. Many survey questions and their corresponding rating scales mirror those of the GHAA's "Consumer Satisfaction Survey." This allows ChoiceCare results to be compared against nationally syndicated benchmark data.

Survey Used to Measure Patient Satisfaction With:

- Quality of medical care received from doctors;
- Customer services;
- Simplicity of educational materials and other materials;
- Outcomes of medical care/how much patient was helped;
- Confidence in doctor's ability to handle the problem;
- Likelihood to recommend.

Type of Patient Completing Survey: Enrollees.

When do Patients/Enrollees Complete Survey?: Patients complete the survey via telephone interview approximately four to 12 weeks after having an office visit.

Background Information Collected on Those Completing the Survey: None.

How are Survey Findings Used?: Results are reported to primary care physicians quarterly on an individual basis as well as a group practice level. Results are used as part of a behavioral incentive program in which physician groups receive incentive moneys based on the level of satisfaction of their ChoiceCare patients. Physician groups whose patient satisfaction scores fall below a set standard are reviewed with the physician and a ChoiceCare Medical Director to determine an action plan for improvement. Results for these groups are monitored to assess improvement. Patient satisfaction scores are also used as part of the re-credentialling process for participating primary care physicians.

Date of Last Revision to Survey: April 1995.

Purchase Price of Survey: ChoiceCare does not sell, lease or rent surveys.

Contact Information: Randy L. Burton, Customer Satisfaction Research Analyst, ChoiceCare, 655 Eden Park Drive, Cincinnati, Ohio 45202, (513) 357-6568; fax (513) 784-5198.

Cleveland Health Quality Choice Program

Cleveland, Ohio

Title of Survey: NCG Research's "Your Hospital Stay: The Patient's Viewpoint" (See **NCG Research** entry.)

Profile of Organization: Cleveland Health Quality Choice is a coalition of businesses, hospitals and physicians formed in 1989 to support the goals of health care reform.

Date Survey was Created: N/A

Overview of Survey: The survey, designed by NCG Research, collects data on hospital stays, reasons why a patient chose a specific hospital, the time it took to gain admission, the perceived amount of pain from which a patient suffered, and the amount of help a patient required to perform ordinary activities. The survey also determines if a patient remained well informed as to his/her condition, satisfaction with physicians, nurses and ancillary staff, living arrangements, and billing.

Survey Used to Measure Patient Satisfaction With:

- Quality of medical care received from doctors, health plans and hospitals;
- Customer services;
- Costs of care;
- Access to care;
- Coverage;
- Simplicity of educational and other materials;
- Simplicity of paperwork.

Type of Patient Completing Survey: All inpatient discharges except those discharged against medical advice.

When do Patients/Enrollees Complete Survey?: Twice annually.

Background Information Collected on Those Completing the Survey: N/A

How are Survey Findings Used?: Overall quality improvements.

Date of Last Revision to Survey: N/A

Purchase Price of Survey: N/A

Contact Information: Quality Information Management Corporation, Statler Office Tower, Suite 741, 1127 Euclid Avenue, Cleveland, Ohio 44115, (216) 696-7999; fax: (216) 696-0007.

Community Health Plan
Latham, N.Y.

Title of Survey: Fact Finders Member Satisfaction Survey

Profile of Organization: Community Health Plan operates a mixed model, nonprofit health plan with over 370,000 enrollees in upstate New York, Vermont and Western Massachusetts.

Date Survey was Created: 1994.

Overview of Survey: Since October 1994, CHP has contracted with Fact Finders, Inc., an Albany-based public opinion and market research firm, to conduct telephone surveys of members. Each quarter, CHP provides Fact Finders with a list of members who have visited their primary care providers in the previous three months, and members who had a visit in the prior quarter for which a claim was filed in the most recent period. Each month, a random sample of 1,000 of those members is drawn by Fact Finders.

Survey Used to Measure Patient Satisfaction With:
- Quality of medical care received from doctors and health plans;
- Access to care;
- Thoroughness of care;
- Correct diagnosis;
- Amount of time spent during visit listening to patient concerns;
- Explanation of treatment in words patient can understand;
- Patient involvement in medical decisions;
- Advice on improving health.

Type of Patient Completing Survey: Survey involves approximately 1,000 members who have been seen within the previous 90 days, randomly selected from all CHP practices with 100 or more members. Members in practices of less than 100 are put in a separate category and will not be reported at the practice level.

When do Patients/Enrollees Complete Survey?: See Overview.

Background Information Collected on Those Completing the Survey: None.

How are Survey Findings Used?: Detailed plan-wide and regional results are compiled quarterly. Practice group level results are aggregated semi-annually for the largest practices and health centers, and annually for all practices with 100 or more CHP members.

Date of Last Revision to Survey: January 1996.

Purchase Price of Survey: Not for sale.

Contact Information: Proposal Services, Community Health Plan, 1 CHP Plaza, Latham, N.Y. 12302, (518) 783-1864; fax (518) 782-1864.

Colorado Department of Health Care Policy and Financing

Denver, Colo.

Title of Survey: The Colorado Medicaid Primary Care Physician Program Patient Survey

Profile of Organization: The Colorado Department of Health Care Policy and Financing is responsible for administering the federal-state Medicaid program and improving access, quality and cost effectiveness of health care services for all Coloradans.

Date Survey was Created: N/A

Overview of Survey: Survey contains 39 questions regarding satisfaction with and access to care.

Survey Used to Measure Patient Satisfaction With:

- Quality of medical care received from doctors;
- Customer services;
- Access to care.

Type of Patient Completing Survey: A sample of enrollees.

When do Patients/Enrollees Complete Survey?: Biannually.

Background Information Collected on Those Completing the Survey: Demographic, including age, sex, primary language spoken and geographic location.

How are Survey Findings Used?: Results are reported to HCFA to continue operation of 1915(b) waiver, and reviewed for quality improvement enhancements.

Date of Last Revision to Survey: January 1996.

Purchase Price of Survey: N/A

Contact Information: Reid Reynolds, Colorado Department of Health Care Policy and Financing, 1575 Sherman Street, Denver, Colo. 80203, (303) 866-2158; fax (303) 866-2803.

THE COLORADO MEDICAID PRIMARY CARE PHYSICIAN PROGRAM

PLEASE FILL OUT THIS SURVEY FOR THE PERSON TO WHOM THE SURVEY IS ADDRESSED. If it is addressed to a child, please fill it out for the child regarding the care he/she receives.

Please fill out this survey for the person to whom the survey is addressed. Please answer all the questions to the best of your ability.

The county that you live in _____

Your name _____

Your Medicaid identification number (example:D123456) _____

Your Doctor or clinic's name and address _____

Your Doctor or clinic's phone number_____

_____

On average, please rate your health care based on the following statements:

Circle the number that corresponds with your answer.

I. SATISIFACTION WITH CARE	Strongly Disagree	Disagree	Neither Agree or Disagree	Agree	Strongly Agree
1. I can get an appointment with my doctor or clinic when I want one.	1	2	3	4	5
2. I can see my doctor or medical staff at my clinic when I have an urgent problem.	1	2	3	4	5
3. My doctor or medical staff at my clinic are available to answer my questions and give me advice.	1	2	3	4	5
4. My doctor or medical staff at my clinic refer me to a specialist when I need one.	1	2	3	4	5
5. I am satisfied with the amount of time I usually spend in the waiting room or lobby at my doctor's office or clinic.	1	2	3	4	5
6. I am satisified with the amount of time I wait in the examination room to see my doctor or clinic.	1	2	3	4	5
7. My doctor listens and responds to my concerns about my illness or condition.	1	2	3	4	5

	Stongly Disagree	Disagree	Neither Agree or Disagree	Agree	Strongly Agree
8. My doctor or medical staff at my clinic are interested in me and my medical problems.	1	2	3	4	5
9. My doctor or medical staff at my clinic treat me with respect and give me privacy when I need it.	1	2	3	4	5
10. In general, my doctor, or medical staff at my clinic, spend the right amount of time with me.	1	2	3	4	5
11. Overall, I am satisified with the quality of medical care I receive.	1	2	3	4	5
12. My doctor, or medical staff at my clinic, give me a complete exam for the condition I see him/her for.	1	2	3	4	5
13. My doctor, or medical staff at my clinic, explain medical procedures, tests, and medical conditions or diagnoses to me.	1	2	3	4	5
14. My doctor, or medical staff at my clinic, give me advice about ways to avoid illness and stay healthy.	1	2	3	4	5
15. My doctor, or medical staff at my clinic, tell me how to get care when the office is closed.	1	2	3	4	5
16. I am generally satisifed with the quality of service I receive from the medical staff at my doctor's office or clinic.	1	2	3	4	5
17. If I call my doctor or medical staff at my clinic, the call is returned promptly.	1	2	3	4	5
18. The office staff is usually pleasant to me.	1	2	3	4	5
19. Overall, I am satisfied with my primary care doctor.	1	2	3	4	5

III. ACCESS TO CARE

20. If **your child** needed to get care for the following medical problems, what would you most likely do?	Call doctor for advice	Go Straight to doctor's office	Go to Hospital emergency room	Treat at home	Not Sure
a. pain in child's ear	1	2	3	4	5
b. child temporarily unconscious after a fall	1	2	3	4	5
c. skin rash on child's wrist	1	2	3	4	5
d. child's fever of 104 degrees	1	2	3	4	5

21. If **you** needed to get care for the following medical problems, what would you most likely do?					
a. back pain	1	2	3	4	5
b. severe chest pain	1	2	3	4	5
c. shortness of breath	1	2	3	4	5
d. blood in urine	1	2	3	4	5

	Your own car	a friend's car	cab	public bus	other
22. What transportation do you usually use to get to your primary care doctor's office?	1	2	3	4	5
23. What transportation do you usually use to get to the nearest emergency room?	1	2	3	4	5

24. About how many miles is it to your primary care doctor's office or clinic?

_____miles   _____don't know

25. About how many minutes does it take to get to your primary care doctor's office or clinic?

_____miles   _____don't know

26. About how many miles is it to the nearest hospital emergency room?

_____miles   _____don't know

27. About how many minutes does it take to get to the nearest hospital emergency room?

_____minutes   _____don't know

28. When you call the doctor's office or clinic to make an appointment, how many days does it take before you can get in:

   (a) for a routine visit? _____days   _____don't know
   (b) for an urgent visit? _____days   _____don't know
   (c) for follow-up to an office visit? _____days   _____don't know
   (d) for follow-up to an emergency room visit_____days _____don't know
   (e) I have never tried to make an appointment with my primary care doctor._____

29. When you call your doctor or clinic during the day Monday through Friday (8:00 am - 5:00 pm) with an urgent call, how long does it take for he/she to call you back?

   (a) More than 3 hours
   (b) More than 2 hours less than 3 hours
   (c) More than 1 hour less than 2 hours
   (d) More than 30 minutes less than 1 hour
   (e) 30 minutes or less

30. When you call your doctor or clinic after hours (after 5:00 pm, Monday through Friday or on the weekend) how long does it take for he/she to call you back?

   (a) More than 3 hours
   (b) More than 2 hours less than 3 hours
   (c) More than 1 hour less than 2 hours
   (d) More than 30 minutes less than 1 hour
   (e) 30 minutes or less

(Please circle one letter to answer each of the following questions:)

31. How long to you have to wait in the exam room before you see your doctor?

   a. more than 60 minutes
   b. more than 45 minutes less than 60 minutes
   c. more than 30 minutes less than 45 minutes
   d. more than 15 minutes less than 30 minutes
   e. less than 15 minutes

32. How long have you been participating with Medicaid? (We are interested in the total time you have been on Medicaid, for example 6 months in 1994, 10 months in 1995=over a year total time)

   a. Less than 6 months
   b. 6 months to 1 year
   c. More than 1 year, but less than 3 years
   d. 3 years but less than 5 years
   e. 5 years or more
   f. I don't know or can't remember

33. How long have you had a primary care doctor listed on your Medicaid card?

    a. Less than 6 months
    b. 6 months to 1 year
    c. More than 1 year, but less than 3 years
    d. 3 years but less than 5 years
    e. 5 years or more
    f. I don't know or can't remember

34. Where would you most likely go to fill a prescription?

    a. Drug store or pharmacy
    b. Doctor's office or clinic
    c. Emergency room

35. Where did you pick your primary care doctor?

    a. PCPP Hotline - I called in my choice
    b. PCPP Hotline - I mailed in my choice
    c. County Department of Social Services
    d. Presumptive Eligibility Site
    e. Social Security Office
    f. PCP was assigned to me

36. How long has your doctor been your primary care doctor?

    a. less than a year
    b. More than one year but less than two years
    c. More than two years but less than three years
    d. three years or more
    e. I do not have a primary care doctor.

37. How aware were you that the PCP Program has a complaint process?

    a. Very aware
    b. Somewhat aware
    c. Not aware

38. If you have ever made a complaint, if so what happened?

39. If you have any comments about your primary care doctor, please write them here:

If you would like to be contacted about the following programs, please check the appropriate line, give your name and address and information will be sent.

_____WIC _____EPSDT (Children's Program) ____Birth Control ____Help to find a PCP

_____Additional Information on _____

Name & Address:

For classification purposes only:

Sex of the participant   _____Male ____Female

Age of the participant (Please check the line that corresponds to the age of the person who the survey was filled out for

____ 0-5	____ 15-18	____ 26-35	____ 55-64
____ 6-8	____ 19-21	____ 36-45	____ 65 and older
____ 9-14	____ 22-25	____ 46-55	

Is English your primary language? ____yes ____no

      If not, what is your primary language?_____

Do you have access to a telephone?_____

Thank you for your help! Your participation is valued.

`For office use only:`

Please fold survey in half, staple and drop in mail. Postage is prepaid by Medicaid.

Colorado Department of Health Care Policy and Financing

Denver, Colo.

Title of Survey: The Colorado Medicaid Managed Care Program Patient Survey

Profile of Organization: The Colorado Department of Health Care Policy and Financing is responsible for administering the federal-state Medicaid program and improving access, quality and cost effectiveness of health care services for all Coloradans.

Date Survey was Created: N/A

Overview of Survey: Survey contains 39 questions regarding satisfaction with and access to care.

Survey Used to Measure Patient Satisfaction With:

- Quality of care received from doctors and the HMO;
- Customer services;
- Access to care.

Type of Patient Completing Survey: A sample of enrollees.

When do Patients/Enrollees Complete Survey?: Annually.

Background Information Collected on Those Completing the Survey: Demographic, including primary language spoken and geographic area.

How are Survey Findings Used?: Results are reported to HCFA to continue operation of 1915(b) waiver, and reviewed for quality improvement enhancements.

Date of Last Revision to Survey: October 1995.

Purchase Price of Survey: N/A

Contact Information: Reid Reynolds, Colorado Department of Health Care Policy and Financing, 1525 Sherman Street, Denver, Colo. 80203, (303) 866-2158; fax (303) 866-2803.

THE COLORADO MEDICAID
MANAGED CARE PROGRAM

<u>PLEASE FILL OUT THIS SURVEY FOR THE PERSON TO WHOM THE SURVEY IS ADDRESSED</u>. If it is addressed to a child, please fill out for the child regarding the care he/she receives. <u>Please answer all the questions to the best of your ability</u>.

Thomas Johnson   Medicaid identification number : *D123456*

Your doctor's or clinic's name and address: _____

_____

Your doctor's or clinic's phone number: _____

Is *COMMUNITY HEALTH PLAN OF THE ROCKIES* still your current plan?   ____ yes   ____ no

Please answer the following questions for *COMMUNITY HEALTH PLAN OF THE ROCKIES*, even if you no longer participate in that plan.

On average, please rate your health care based on the following statements.

<u>Circle</u> the number that corresponds with your answer.

I. SATISFACTION WITH CARE	Strongly Disagree	Disagree	Neither Agree nor Disagree	Agree	Strongly Agree
1. I can get an appointment with my doctor when I want one.	1	2	3	4	5
2. I can see my doctor when I have an urgent problem.	1	2	3	4	5
3. My doctor is available to answer my questions and give me advice.	1	2	3	4	5
4. My doctor refers me to a specialist when I need one.	1	2	3	4	5
5. I am satisfied with the amount of time I usually spend in the waiting room.	1	2	3	4	5
6. I am satisfied with the amount of time I wait in the examination room to see my doctor.	1	2	3	4	5

D123456 - B   1

	Strongly Disagree	Disagree	Neither Agree nor Disagree	Agree	Strongly Agree
7. My doctor listens and responds to my concerns about my illness or condition.	1	2	3	4	5
8. My doctor is interested in me and my medical problems.	1	2	3	4	5
9. My doctor treats me with respect and gives me privacy when I need it.	1	2	3	4	5
10. My doctor spends the right amount of time with me.	1	2	3	4	5
11. Overall, I am satisfied with the quality of medical care I receive.	1	2	3	4	5
12. My doctor gives me a complete exam for the condition I see him for.	1	2	3	4	5
13. My doctor explains medical procedures, tests, and medical conditions or diagnoses to me.	1	2	3	4	5
14. My doctor gives me advice about ways to avoid illness and stay healthy.	1	2	3	4	5
15. My doctor tells me how to get care when the office is closed.	1	2	3	4	5
16. I am satisfied with the quality of service I receive from the non-physician medical staff at my doctor's office (example: physician's assistant, nurse, etc.).	1	2	3	4	5
17. If I call my doctor, he or she returns my call promptly.	1	2	3	4	5
18. The office staff is usually pleasant to me.	1	2	3	4	5
19. Overall, I am satisfied with my primary care doctor.	1	2	3	4	5

D123456 - B

2

23

	Strongly Disagree	Disagree	Neither Agree nor Disagree	Agree	Strongly Agree
20. Overall, I am satisfied with *COMMUNITY HEALTH PLAN OF THE ROCKIES*	1	2	3	4	5

II. ACCESS TO CARE

21. If your youngest **child** needed to get care Monday through Friday for the following medical problems, what would you be most likely to do?

	call doctor for advice	go straight to doctor's office	go to hospital emergency room	treat at home	not sure
a) pain in child's ear	1	2	3	4	5
b) child temporarily unconscious after a fall	1	2	3	4	5
c) skin rash on child's wrist	1	2	3	4	5
d) child's fever of 104 degrees	1	2	3	4	5

22. If **you** needed to get care Monday through Friday for the following medical problems, what would you be most likely to do?

	call doctor for advice	go straight to doctor's office	go to hospital emergency room	treat at home	not sure
a) back pain	1	2	3	4	5
b) severe chest pain	1	2	3	4	5
c) shortness of breath	1	2	3	4	5
d) blood in urine	1	2	3	4	5

23. What transportation do you usually use to get to your primary care **doctor's office?**

a) your own car
b) a friend's car
c) public bus
d) other (describe)_____

24. What transportation do you usually use to get to the nearest **emergency room**?

a) your own car
b) a friend's car
c) public bus
d) other (describe)_____

25. About how many miles is it to your primary care doctor's office? _____ miles _____ don't know

26. About how many minutes does it take to get to your
primary care doctor's office? _____ minutes _____ don't know

27. About how many miles is it to the nearest hospital
emergency room? _____ miles _____ don't know

28. About how many minutes does it take to get to the nearest
hospital emergency room? _____ minutes _____ don't know

29. When you call the doctor's office to make an appointment, how many days is it before you can get in:

a) for a routine visit? _____ days _____ don't know

b) for an urgent visit? _____ days _____ don't know

c) for follow-up to an office visit? _____ days _____ don't know

d) for follow-up to an emergency room visit? _____ days _____ don't know

e) I have never tried to make an appointment with my primary care doctor. _____

Please check one line to answer each of the following questions:

30. How long in total have you been participating with Medicaid? (We are interested in the total time you have been on Medicaid. For example, if it was 6 months in 1993 and 9 months in 1994, it would total 15 months, and you would check number 3.)

1) ____ Less than 6 months
2) ____ More than 6 months but less than 1 year
3) ____ More than 1 year but less than 3 years
4) ____ More than 3 years but less than 5 years
5) ____ 5 years or more
6) ____ I don't know or can't remember

31. How long in total have you been a member of *COMMUNITY HEALTH PLAN OF THE ROCKIES* ?

    1) _____ Less than 6 months
    2) _____ More than 6 months but less than 1 year
    3) _____ More than 1 year but less than 3 years
    4) _____ More than 3 years but less than 5 years
    5) _____ 5 years or more
    6) _____ I don't know or can't remember

32. How many different HMOs (Managed Care Plans) have you been a part of during the last year?

    1) _____ One
    2) _____ Two
    3) _____ Three
    4) _____ More than three
    5) _____ I don't know or can't remember

33. Where would you be most likely to go to fill a prescription?

    1) _____ Drug store or pharmacy
    2) _____ Doctor's office
    3) _____ Emergency room

34. How long has your doctor been your primary care doctor?

    1) _____ Less than 1 year
    2) _____ More than one year but less than 2 years
    3) _____ More than 2 years but less than 3 years
    4) _____ 3 years or more
    5) _____ I don't have a primary care doctor
    6) _____ I don't know or can't remember

35. How was your primary care doctor selected?

    1) _____ I chose my doctor.
    2) _____ The HMO assigned my doctor to me.
    3) _____ It was the same doctor I had before I joined the HMO.
    4) _____ I don't have a primary care doctor.

36. Where did you usually get health care before joining the HMO?

    1) _____ From the same doctor
    2) _____ From another doctor
    3) _____ From a community health center
    4) _____ From the hospital emergency room
    5) _____ Other (describe: _____)

37. Do all members of your family belong to *COMMUNITY HEALTH PLAN OF THE ROCKIES ?*
    _____ yes   _____ no

38. If family members use more than one HMO (Managed Care Plan), please explain why:
    _____
    _____

39. If you have any comments about your primary care doctor or the HMO, please write them here:
    _____
    _____
    _____
    _____
    _____

For classification purposes only:

Is English your primary language?   _____ Yes   _____ No

    If not, what is your primary language? _____

Do you have access to a telephone?   _____ Yes   _____ No

Thank you for your help! We appreciate your participation. Please return the survey to Colorado Foundation for Medical Care in the enclosed postage-paid envelope.

D123456 - B   6

Coopers & Lybrand

Boston, Mass.

Title of Survey: Consumer Health Plan Value Survey

Profile of Organization: Coopers & Lybrand is one of the nation's largest business assurance and consulting firms.

Date Survey was Created: September 1995.

Overview of Survey: Survey is a 116-item questionnaire that takes about 10-20 minutes to complete. It first covers employer/enrollee satisfaction with health plan/health care using the kinds of measures listed below. Then, the survey moves to the health domain, again covering the content areas listed below.

Survey Used to Measure Patient Satisfaction With:

- Quality of medical care received from doctors and health plans;
- Costs of care;
- Coverage;
- Physician choice;
- Plan choice;
- Importance of various plan/care attributes;
- Simplicity of paperwork.

Type of Patient Completing Survey: Survey is administered to random samples of covered populations, and includes both recent users and non-users of health care.

When do Patients/Enrollees Complete Survey?: Survey is administered on a mail-out/mail-back basis to respondents' residences. It can be administered at any time of the year.

Background Information Collected on Those Completing the Survey: Employee/enrollee name, address, phone number, plan affiliation, length of enrollment and utilization.

How are Survey Findings Used?: Among uses are evaluating corporate health care strategy, informing employees/enrollees on plan performance, and promoting continuous quality improvements on the part of the plans.

Date of Last Revision to Survey: Summer 1995.

Purchase Price of Survey: N/A

Contact Information: Dr. Harris Allen, Coopers & Lybrand L.L.P./Health Care Survey Unit, One International Place, Boston, Mass. 02110, (617) 478-3419; fax (617) 478-3900; e-mail hallen@colybrand.com

FHP Health Care of Colorado

Englewood, Colo.

Title of Survey: "Open Dialogue" Patient Survey

Profile of Organization: FHP Health Care of Colorado, part of the FHP network, is an HMO serving over 300,000 enrollees in 21 counties, including Denver. It contracts with and/or uses 36 hospitals and one PHO, and has over 2,800 physicians.

Date Survey was Created: 1991.

Overview of Survey: Survey consists of 24 questions to be answered in a 4-minute telephone interview.

Survey Used to Measure Patient Satisfaction With:

- Quality of medical care received from doctors;
- Access to care (time to schedule appointments, time spent in waiting room);
- Access by visit type (emergency, urgent, etc.);
- Physician communications and competence;
- Laboratory services;
- Overall satisfaction with physician and plan.

Type of Patient Completing Survey: Patients are selected randomly from claims encounter data. HMO, POS and Senior Plan members are called. Certain types of diagnoses are excluded as being inappropriate. Member files are screened to ensure only one call per household per year.

When do Patients/Enrollees Complete Survey?: Patients are called within six to eight weeks of an office visit.

Background Information Collected on Those Completing the Survey: Demographic, including age, sex and family size. Primary care physician name, utilization data and health plan.

How are Survey Findings Used?: Through FHP's physician incentive program, recredentialling program and the efforts of FHP Provider Service staff and FHP-contracted physicians, survey data is a useful tool for rewarding and supporting physicians for providing quality care to FHP members.

Date of Last Revision to Survey: April 1996.

Purchase Price of Survey: Not for sale.

Contact Information: Charles Gaughan, Director, Research and Planning, FHP Health Care of Colorado, 6455 South Yosemite, Englewood, Colo. 80111, (800) 877-6685.

George Washington University Health Plan

Bethesda, Md.

Title of Survey: George Washington University Health Plan Member Satisfaction Survey

Profile of Organization: George Washington University Health Plan serves over 72,000 enrollees in the metropolitan Washington, D.C. area. It has seven medical centers, contracts with and/or uses 24 area hospitals and three PHOs, and has over 1,900 physicians.

Date Survey was Created: N/A

Overview of Survey: Two surveys, with one measuring services to adults and the other measuring pediatric services.

Survey Used to Measure Patient Satisfaction With:

- Quality of medical care received from doctors and other providers;
- Customer service;
- Access to care;
- Confidence in care.

Type of Patient Completing Survey: Patients seen in previous 6-month period.

When do Patients/Enrollees Complete Survey?: After appointment.

Background Information Collected on Those Completing the Survey: Age; sex; marital status; education; race; length of time as member; number of visits.

How are Survey Findings Used?: Presented to Oversight Committee on a quarterly basis.

Date of Last Revision to Survey: 1992.

Purchase Price of Survey: N/A

Contact Information: Anne Owens, Survey Coordinator, George Washington University Health Plan, 4550 Montgomery Avenue, Suite 800, Bethesda, Md. 20814, (301) 941-2175; fax (301) 941-2008.

The George Washington University
Health Plan
VIRGINIA · WASHINGTON DC · MARYLAND

4/2/96

GEORGE WASHINGTON UNIVERSITY MEMBER SATISFACTION SURVEY

Our records indicate you recently had an appointment at the Health Plan with **Dr. George Washington**. Please complete the following survey to help us assess your satisfaction with your health care. The survey is anonymous so please respond openly. Your responses are important to our efforts at improving the quality of services at the Health Plan. Please feel free to write additional comments below.

What was the reason for your recent visit?

_____ History & Physical Appointment   _____ Urgent Appointment
_____ Regularly Scheduled Appointment   _____ Walk-in (No appt)

HOW WOULD YOU RATE THE FOLLOWING? *(Please Circle One Number On Each Line)*

	Does Not Apply	Poor	Fair	Good	Very Good	Excellent
	0	1	2	3	4	5

ACCESS TO CARE

Able to get through on the phone	0	1	2	3	4	5
Able to obtain appointment in a timely manner	0	1	2	3	4	5
Waiting time in reception area	0	1	2	3	4	5
Waiting time in exam room	0	1	2	3	4	5
Ease of seeing the provider of your choice	0	1	2	3	4	5

COURTESY AND CONSIDERATION
Manner in which you were treated:

Receptionist	0	1	2	3	4	5
Nursing Assistant	0	1	2	3	4	5
Provider	0	1	2	3	4	5

PROVIDER
Willingness of your Provider to:

Listen patiently and answer questions	0	1	2	3	4	5
Spend enough time with you	0	1	2	3	4	5
Thoroughness of examination and assessment	0	1	2	3	4	5

SATISFACTION

	Does Not Apply	Poor	Fair	Good	Very Good	Excellent
	0	1	2	3	4	5
How satisfied were you with: The care you received on this last visit?	0	1	2	3	4	5
Overall care you have received at the Health Plan	0	1	2	3	4	5

PERSONAL PROFILE

About how long have you been a patient in the George Washington University Health Plan: _____ years.

About how many visits have you made to the George Washington University Health Plan in the past 12 months: _____

What is your age? _____   Sex: _____ Male _____ Female

What is your race: _____ White _____ Black _____ Asian _____ Hispanic _____ Other

What is the highest level of education you have completed:

_____ High School   _____ College
_____ Some College   _____ Post college grad degree

Marital status: _____ Single _____ Married _____ Divorced _____ Widowed

COMMENTS (Please use the other side for further comments or suggestions)

What do you like most about the Health Plan?

What area would you like the Health Plan most to improve upon?

4/2/96

GEORGE WASHINGTON UNIVERSITY MEMBER SATISFACTION SURVEY

Our records indicate that your child recently had an appointment at the Health Plan with Dr. Martha Washington. Please complete the following survey to help us assess your satisfaction with your child's health care. The survey is anonymous so please respond openly. Your responses are important to our efforts at improving the quality of services. Please feel free to write additional comments below or on the back.

What was the reason for your child's recent visit?

___ History & Physical Appt "Check-Up"	___ Urgent Appt "Sick Visit"
___ Regularly Scheduled Appt "Follow-up"	___ Walk-in (No appt)

HOW WOULD YOU RATE THE FOLLOWING? *(Please Circle One Number On Each Line)*

	Does Not Apply	Poor	Fair	Good	Very Good	Excellent
ACCESS TO CARE						
Able to get through on the phone	0	1	2	3	4	5
Able to obtain appointment in a timely manner	0	1	2	3	4	5
Waiting time in reception area	0	1	2	3	4	5
Waiting time in exam rm	0	1	2	3	4	5
Ease of seeing the pediatrician of your choice	0	1	2	3	4	5
COURTESY AND CONSIDERATION						
Manner in which your child was treated:						
Receptionist	0	1	2	3	4	5
Nursing Staff	0	1	2	3	4	5
Pediatrician	0	1	2	3	4	5
PROVIDER						
Willingness of your child's Pediatrician to:						
Listen patiently and answer questions	0	1	2	3	4	5
Spend enough time with you and your child	0	1	2	3	4	5
Thoroughness of examination and assessment	0	1	2	3	4	5
Provide helpful explanation or advice	0	1	2	3	4	5

	Does Not Apply	Poor	Fair	Good	Very Good	Excellent
SATISFACTION						
How satisfied were you with:						
The care your child received on this last visit?	0	1	2	3	4	5
Overall care your child has recvd at the Health Plan	0	1	2	3	4	5
How did your child like the visit	0	1	2	3	4	5

What is your child's age? _____ Sex: ___ Male ___ Female

About how many visits has your child made to the George Washington University Health Plan in the past 12 months: _____

PARENT PROFILE

About how long have you been a member in the George Washington University Health Plan: _____ years.

What is your age? _____ Sex: ___ Male ___ Female

What is your race: ___ White ___ Black ___ Asian ___ Hispanic ___ Other

What is the highest level of education you have completed:

___ High School ___ College ___ Some College ___ Post college grad degree

Marital status: ___ Single ___ Married ___ Divorced ___ Widowed

COMMENTS *(Please use the other side for further comments or suggestions)*
What do you like most about the Health Plan?

What area would you like the Health Plan most to improve upon?

GTE

Waltham, Mass.

Title of Survey: Employer Health Care Value Survey

Profile of Organization: GTE is the fourth-largest publicly-owned telecommunications company in the world, with 82,000 active employees and 55,000 retirees participating in its health plans.

Date Survey was Created: 1993.

Overview of Survey: About 40 questions designed, tested and piloted by The Health Institute in Boston.

Survey Used to Measure Patient Satisfaction With:

- Quality of medical care received from doctors and health plans;
- Customer services;
- Costs of care;
- Access to care;
- Coverage;
- Simplicity of educational and other materials;
- Simplicity of paperwork.

Type of Patient Completing Survey: GTE employees use the survey to measure satisfaction with hospital stays, primary care providers and physician office visits.

When do Patients/Enrollees Complete Survey?: Once every two years based on a random sample.

Background Information Collected on Those Completing the Survey: Functional status; detailed satisfaction and access information related to disease state; lifestyle factors; age; sex; other demographic information.

How are Survey Findings Used?: To rate plans and report back to employees; to drive CQI at plans; plan selection.

Date of Last Revision to Survey: October 1995.

Purchase Price of Survey: N/A

Contact Information: Sue Sheffler, GTE Service Corp, 40 Sylvan Road, Waltham, Mass. 02254, (617) 466-2326; fax (617) 466-2856.

Harvard Pilgrim Health Care

Boston, Mass.

Title of Survey: Member Survey

Profile of Organization: Harvard Pilgrim Health Care, the result of a merger between Harvard Community Health Plan and Pilgrim Health Care, Inc., serves over 565,000 enrollees in Massachusetts, Rhode Island and New Hampshire.

Date Survey was Created: 1995.

Overview of Survey: The four-page survey contains approximately 100 questions. Actual survey length varies depending on which questions are skipped based on respondent experience with the plan. The survey contains nine main categories: provider choice, quality of care, patient-physician communication, access to care, customer service (medical offices), customer service (administrative areas), convenience of medical offices, coverage and cost. The survey also measures overall satisfaction with the plan, as well as collects general demographic information. A separate study is conducted with members under 65 years of age. A second study is conducted with Medicare members who are over the age of 65. In all cases, members are randomly selected to participate in the studies regardless of past experience or usage.

Survey Used to Measure Patient Satisfaction With:

- Quality of medical care received from doctors and health plans;
- Access to care;
- Costs of care;
- Coverage.

Type of Patient Completing Survey: N/A

When do Patients/Enrollees Complete Survey?: N/A

Background Information Collected on Those Completing the Survey: N/A

How are Survey Findings Used?: The information collected is used by the plan's management to track performance over time and to identify areas needing improvement. Overall, the survey is used for quality improvement purposes throughout the plan where applicable.

Date of Last Revision to Survey: N/A

Purchase Price of Survey: N/A

Contact Information: Antonio Ferreira, Harvard Pilgrim Health Care, 3 Allied Drive, Needham, Mass. 02026-6121, (617) 251-1725; fax (617) 251-1888.

 Harvard Community Health Plan

 Harvard Community Health Plan *of New England*

MEMBER SURVEY

The opinions of *all* our members are important to us as we work to provide members with high quality medical care and service. You can help us determine how well we are serving your health care needs and how to improve our services by taking just a few minutes to complete this questionnaire. If the envelope is addressed to your child, please complete the questionnaire with your child's health care in mind. Otherwise, please complete the questionnaire based on your experiences. We would like your opinions about your care to be based on the primary medical site/doctor's office that you (or your child) had the most experience with during the past year. Be assured that your answers and comments will remain confidential and reported in summary form only. Please return this questionnaire in the enclosed, postage-paid envelope. Thank you for letting us know how well we are doing in meeting your health care needs.

1a. Are you currently a member of Harvard Community Health Plan (HCHP)/Harvard Community Health Plan of New England (HCHP-NE)?

❑₁ Yes *(Please continue)*
❑₂ No *(Thank you. Please return this questionnaire in the enclosed envelope.)*

1b. Are you completing this questionnaire for yourself or your child?

❑₁ Yourself   ❑₂ Your child

2. How long have you been a member of HCHP/HCHP-NE? __ years. *(If Less Than One Year, Write '0'.)*

3. Do you have a primary care doctor, that is, a doctor whom you rely on for most of your care at HCHP/HCHP-NE?

❑₁ Yes
❑₂ No
❑₃ Don't know

4a. During the past year, approximately how many visits have you made to HCHP/HCHP-NE? _____
(If None, Write '0' and Skip To Question 5)

4b. When was your most recent visit to your HCHP/HCHP-NE medical site/doctor's office during the past year? *(Check Only One)*

❑₁ Within past 3 months
❑₂ Over 3, but within 6 months
❑₈ Over 6, but within 9 months
❑₄ Over 9, but within 12 months

4c. Have you switched primary care physicians since your last visit with the doctor?

❑¹ Yes *(Skip to Question 6)*
❑² No *(Skip to Question 6)*

5. Since you enrolled in HCHP/HCHP-NE, have you used medical services covered by the plan?

❑₁ Yes
❑₂ No

6. We would like to know how you feel about various aspects of HCHP/HCHP-NE and your medical site/doctor's office. For each item, please mark how you feel about your medical site/doctor's office experience *during the past year* in the appropriate box.

6A. PROVIDER CHOICE

	EXCELLENT	VERY GOOD	GOOD	FAIR	POOR	NOT APPLICABLE
• Number of doctors you have to choose from	❑	❑	❑	❑	❑	❑
• Availability of doctors accepting new patients	❑	❑	❑	❑	❑	❑
• Hospitals that are available through HCHP/HCHP-NE	❑	❑	❑	❑	❑	❑

• How satisfied are you with the *choice of providers* available through HCHP/HCHP-NE?

❑₅ Very Satisfied   ❑₂ Somewhat Dissatisfied
❑₄ Somewhat Satisfied   ❑₁ Very Dissatisfied
❑₃ Neither Satisfied nor Dissatisfied   ❑₉ Not Applicable

6B. QUALITY OF CARE

	EXCELLENT	VERY GOOD	GOOD	FAIR	POOR	NOT APPLICABLE
• Quality of doctors	❑	❑	❑	❑	❑	❑
• Skill and experience of doctors	❑	❑	❑	❑	❑	❑
• Quality of other clinical staff (nurse practitioners, physician assistants, nurse midwives)	❑	❑	❑	❑	❑	❑
• Advice given about ways to avoid illness and stay healthy	❑	❑	❑	❑	❑	❑
• Amount of personal control you have over decisions affecting your medical care	❑	❑	❑	❑	❑	❑
• Accuracy of diagnosis	❑	❑	❑	❑	❑	❑
• Thoroughness of examinations	❑	❑	❑	❑	❑	❑
• Thoroughness of treatment	❑	❑	❑	❑	❑	❑
• Coordination of your care among all who take care of you	❑	❑	❑	❑	❑	❑
• Outcomes of your medical care, how much you are helped	❑	❑	❑	❑	❑	❑
• Communication of test results	❑	❑	❑	❑	❑	❑

• How satisfied are you with the *quality of care* you receive from HCHP/HCHP-NE?

❑₅ Very Satisfied   ❑₂ Somewhat Dissatisfied
❑₄ Somewhat Satisfied   ❑₁ Very Dissatisfied
❑₃ Neither Satisfied nor Dissatisfied   ❑₉ Not Applicable

6C. PATIENT-PHYSICIAN COMMUNICATION

	EXCELLENT	VERY GOOD	GOOD	FAIR	POOR	NOT APPLICABLE
• Amount of time the doctor spends with you	☐	☐	☐	☐	☐	☐
• Attention given to what you have to say by the doctor	☐	☐	☐	☐	☐	☐
• Doctor inquires thoroughly into your health concerns	☐	☐	☐	☐	☐	☐
• Reassurance offered to you by the doctor	☐	☐	☐	☐	☐	☐
• Willingness of doctor to provide explanations/answer questions	☐	☐	☐	☐	☐	☐
• Explanations given to you about necessary follow-up care (e.g. tests, medicine, procedures)	☐	☐	☐	☐	☐	☐
• Courteousness of doctor(s)	☐	☐	☐	☐	☐	☐

• How satisfied are you with the *communication* you have with the physician(s) at HCHP/HCHP-NE?

☐ 5 Very Satisfied ☐ 2 Somewhat Dissatisfied
☐ 4 Somewhat Satisfied ☐ 1 Very Dissatisfied
☐ 3 Neither Satisfied nor Dissatisfied ☐ 9 Not Applicable

6D. ACCESS TO CARE

	EXCELLENT	VERY GOOD	GOOD	FAIR	POOR	NOT APPLICABLE
• Ease of scheduling medical appointments by phone	☐	☐	☐	☐	☐	☐
• Ease of seeing a doctor when you need to	☐	☐	☐	☐	☐	☐
• Ease of seeing your own doctor	☐	☐	☐	☐	☐	☐
• Ability to see the same doctor on most visits	☐	☐	☐	☐	☐	☐
• Ease of seeing other clinical staff (nurse practitioner, physician assistant, nurse midwife)	☐	☐	☐	☐	☐	☐
• Amount of time you have to wait to get a *routine* appointment	☐	☐	☐	☐	☐	☐
• Convenience of office hours that appointments are available	☐	☐	☐	☐	☐	☐
• Ability to obtain a referral to a specialist	☐	☐	☐	☐	☐	☐
• Amount of time you have to wait for a *specialist* appointment	☐	☐	☐	☐	☐	☐
• Amount of time you have to wait in the *waiting room* for a scheduled appointment	☐	☐	☐	☐	☐	☐
• Amount of time you have to wait in the *exam room* for a scheduled appointment	☐	☐	☐	☐	☐	☐
• Ease of getting care for an illness without an appointment when the doctor's office is *open*	☐	☐	☐	☐	☐	☐
• Ease of getting care without an appointment for an illness when the doctor's office is *closed* (nights & weekends)	☐	☐	☐	☐	☐	☐
• Access to emergency care when you need it	☐	☐	☐	☐	☐	☐

• How satisfied are you with your *access* to medical care at HCHP/HCHP-NE?

☐ 5 Very Satisfied ☐ 2 Somewhat Dissatisfied
☐ 4 Somewhat Satisfied ☐ 1 Very Dissatisfied
☐ 3 Neither Satisfied nor Dissatisfied ☐ 9 Not Applicable

6E. CUSTOMER SERVICE (MEDICAL OFFICES)

	EXCELLENT	VERY GOOD	GOOD	FAIR	POOR	NOT APPLICABLE
• Ease of paying visit co-payments	☐	☐	☐	☐	☐	☐
• Ease of checking in for an appointment	☐	☐	☐	☐	☐	☐
• Courteousness of office/reception staff in the doctor's office	☐	☐	☐	☐	☐	☐
• Ease of getting through to the doctor's office by telephone	☐	☐	☐	☐	☐	☐
• Courteousness of telephone service in the doctor's office	☐	☐	☐	☐	☐	☐
• Length of time put on hold by the doctor's office	☐	☐	☐	☐	☐	☐
• Ease of getting medical advice over the phone when ill	☐	☐	☐	☐	☐	☐
• Amount of time it takes to receive a callback when the doctor's office is *open*	☐	☐	☐	☐	☐	☐
• Amount of time it takes to receive a callback when the doctor's office is *closed*	☐	☐	☐	☐	☐	☐
• Availability of answers to questions about covered HCHP/HCHP-NE benefits or services	☐	☐	☐	☐	☐	☐
• Ability to resolve your complaints/problems	☐	☐	☐	☐	☐	☐

• How satisfied are you with the *service* you receive from your HCHP/HCHP-NE physician(s)/medical office(s)?

☐ 5 Very Satisfied ☐ 2 Somewhat Dissatisfied
☐ 4 Somewhat Satisfied ☐ 1 Very Dissatisfied
☐ 3 Neither Satisfied nor Dissatisfied ☐ 9 Not Applicable

6F. CONVENIENCE (MEDICAL OFFICES)

	EXCELLENT	VERY GOOD	GOOD	FAIR	POOR	NOT APPLICABLE
• Location	☐	☐	☐	☐	☐	☐
• Hours of operation	☐	☐	☐	☐	☐	☐
• Parking	☐	☐	☐	☐	☐	☐
• Physical appearance	☐	☐	☐	☐	☐	☐

• How satisfied are you with the *convenience* of your HCHP/HCHP-NE medical offices?

☐ 5 Very Satisfied ☐ 2 Somewhat Dissatisfied
☐ 4 Somewhat Satisfied ☐ 1 Very Dissatisfied
☐ 3 Neither Satisfied nor Dissatisfied ☐ 9 Not Applicable

6G. CUSTOMER SERVICE (ADMINISTRATIVE AREAS)

	EXCELLENT	VERY GOOD	GOOD	FAIR	POOR	NOT APPLICABLE
• Courteousness of HCHP/HCHP-NE administrative staff when on the phone	☐	☐	☐	☐	☐	☐
• Ease of getting through to HCHP/HCHP-NE administrative area offices by phone	☐	☐	☐	☐	☐	☐
• Length of time put on hold by HCHP/HCHP-NE administrative staff	☐	☐	☐	☐	☐	☐
• Written information provided by HCHP/HCHP-NE about covered benefits or services	☐	☐	☐	☐	☐	☐

6G. CUSTOMER SERVICE *continued* (ADMINISTRATIVE AREAS)

Rating columns: EXCELLENT | VERY GOOD | GOOD | FAIR | POOR | NOT APPLICABLE

- Availability of answers to questions about covered HCHP/HCHP-NE benefits or services □ □ □ □ □ □
- Ability to resolve your complaints/problems □ □ □ □ □ □
- Ease with which claims are handled/paid □ □ □ □ □ □
- Communication of information about how to use HCHP/HCHP-NE services □ □ □ □ □ □
- Information provided to help you choose a personal doctor for your primary care □ □ □ □ □ □

- How satisfied are you with the *customer service* you receive from HCHP/HCHP-NE administrative areas?

☐5 Very Satisfied   ☐2 Somewhat Dissatisfied
☐4 Somewhat Satisfied   ☐1 Very Dissatisfied
☐3 Neither Satisfied nor Dissatisfied   ☐9 Not Applicable

6H. COVERAGE

Rating columns: EXCELLENT | VERY GOOD | GOOD | FAIR | POOR | NOT APPLICABLE

- Coverage for routine/preventive health visits □ □ □ □ □ □
- Coverage for illness visits □ □ □ □ □ □
- Coverage you receive for hospitalization □ □ □ □ □ □
- Coverage in an emergency situation □ □ □ □ □ □
- Coverage when outside HCHP's/HCHP-NE's service area □ □ □ □ □ □

- How satisfied are you with the *coverage* you receive from HCHP/HCHP-NE?

☐5 Very Satisfied   ☐2 Somewhat Dissatisfied
☐4 Somewhat Satisfied   ☐1 Very Dissatisfied
☐3 Neither Satisfied nor Dissatisfied   ☐9 Not Applicable

6I. COST

Rating columns: EXCELLENT | VERY GOOD | GOOD | FAIR | POOR | NOT APPLICABLE

- Cost to you for health care visits (e.g. co-payments) □ □ □ □ □ □
- Cost to you for your health insurance premium (amount deducted from your paycheck) □ □ □ □ □ □
- Cost for prescriptions □ □ □ □ □ □
- Cost to you with respect to the coverage you receive from HCHP/HCHP-NE □ □ □ □ □ □

- How satisfied are you with the *cost* to you for HCHP/HCHP-NE?

☐5 Very Satisfied   ☐2 Somewhat Dissatisfied
☐4 Somewhat Satisfied   ☐1 Very Dissatisfied
☐3 Neither Satisfied nor Dissatisfied   ☐9 Not Applicable

7a. Overall, how satisfied are you with Harvard Community Health Plan/Harvard Community Health Plan of New England?

☐5 Very Satisfied *(Skip to Q 8a)*   ☐2 Somewhat Dissatisfied
☐4 Somewhat Satisfied   ☐1 Very Dissatisfied
☐3 Neither Satisfied nor Dissatisfied   ☐9 Not Applicable *(Skip to Q 8a)*

7b. Why are you less than *very* satisfied?

_____
_____
_____
_____

8a. How likely are you to switch to a different health insurance plan when you next have an opportunity?

☐5 Definitely not switch *(Skip to Q 9)*
☐4 Probably not switch *(Skip to Q 9)*
☐3 Might/might not switch
☐2 Probably switch
☐1 Definitely switch

8b. What are the major reasons you are likely to switch to a different health insurance plan when you next have the opportunity?

_____
_____
_____

9. Considering everything, how likely would you be to recommend HCHP/HCHP-NE to your family or friends?

☐5 Definitely recommend HCHP/HCHP-NE
☐4 Probably recommend HCHP/HCHP-NE
☐3 Might/might not recommend HCHP/HCHP-NE
☐2 Probably not recommend HCHP/HCHP-NE
☐1 Definitely not recommend HCHP/HCHP-NE

10. Who is responsible for making health care decisions in your household?

☐1 Yourself only
☐2 You and your spouse
☐3 Your spouse only
☐4 Other *(Please Specify)*_____

11. How do you currently obtain your health insurance from HCHP/HCHP-NE?

☐1 Through your employer
☐2 Through your spouse's employer
☐3 Through COBRA benefits
☐4 Through a business association
☐5 Through Medicaid and HCHP/HCHP-NE
☐6 Through Medicare and HCHP/HCHP-NE
☐7 Buy directly from HCHP/HCHP-NE
☐8 Other *(Please Specify)*_____

12. What is your present HCHP/HCHP-NE coverage: *(Check only one).*

☐₁ Individual
☐₂ Couple/two person
☐₃ Family

13. How many family members (including yourself) are covered under your HCHP/HCHP-NE insurance?

_____member(s) *(If you only, please write '1'.)*

14. Are you ....?

☐₁ Female
☐₂ Male

15. How old were you on your last birthday?____ years. *(If less than 1 year, write '0'.)*

16. Approximately how long have you been living in this area? _____ years *(If less than 1 year, write '0'.)*

17. Please indicate the highest level of education you have completed.

☐₁ 8th Grade or less
☐₂ Some High school
☐₃ High School Graduate/GED
☐₄ Other Education or Training After High School
☐₅ Some College
☐₆ Two-year college graduate
☐₇ Four-year college graduate
☐₈ Post-Graduate Education or Degree

18. Last year, what was your total family income from all sources (before taxes)?

☐₁ Under $5,000
☐₂ $5,000 - $14,999
☐₃ $15,000 - $24,999
☐₄ $25,000 - $34,999
☐₅ $35,000 - $44,999
☐₆ $45,000 - $59,999
☐₇ $60,000 and over

The following section helps us to ensure that we provide the same level of care to all. Knowing more about you helps us to assess and better meet the needs of a wide variety of our members.

19a. Does anyone in your household have a medical disability that requires some form of accommodation (wheelchair ramp, sign language interpreter, etc.) in order for them to access health care?

☐₁ Yes
☐₂ No *(Skip to Question 20)*

19b. In general, did HCHP/HCHP-NE meet your/their needs?

☐₁ Yes
☐₂ No

19c. Is the accommodation related to:

☐₁ Sight
☐₂ Hearing
☐₃ Mobility
☐₄ Other *(Please Specify)_____*

20. Please check the box(es) that best describes the primary race/ethnicity in your household:

☐₁ Asian or Pacific Islander (having origins in the Far East, Southeast Asia, the Indian subcontinent, or the Pacific Islands)
☐₂ Black/African American (not of Hispanic origin)
☐₃ Hispanic/Latino
☐₄ Native American Indian or Alaskan Native
☐₅ White/Caucasian (not of Hispanic origin)
☐₆ Multi-racial/other *(Please Specify)_____*

21. What language do you speak most often at home?

☐₁ Cantonese
☐₂ English
☐₃ French
☐₄ Greek
☐₅ Haitian Creole
☐₆ Hmong
☐₇ Italian
☐₈ Japanese
☐₉ Khmer
☐₁₀ Laotion
☐₁₁ Mandarin
☐₁₂ Polish
☐₁₃ Portuguese
☐₁₄ Russian
☐₁₅ Spanish
☐₁₆ Vietnamese
☐₁₇ Armenian
☐₁₈ American Sign Language
☐₁₉ Other *(Please Specify)_____*

22. Your personal comments about HCHP/HCHP-NE are very important to us. Please take a few minutes to let us know what you LIKE and DISLIKE about HCHP/HCHP-NE or your medical site/doctor's office.

Medical Site/Doctor's Office *(Please Specify)*

LIKES:

....

....

....

....

DISLIKES:

....

....

....

....

23. If you have a problem or concern that you would like someone from HCHP/HCHP-NE to call you about, please check off the box below and indicate your name and telephone number.

☐ Please call me regarding my problem or concern.

NAME

....

TELEPHONE NO.

....

THANK YOU VERY MUCH for taking the time to answer the questions in this questionnaire.

We appreciate your help in evaluating our services.

Health Alliance Plan of Michigan

Detroit, Mich.

Title of Survey: Health Alliance Plan Subscriber Satisfaction Survey

Profile of Organization: Health Alliance Plan of Michigan is a Detroit-area HMO with over 429,000 enrollees. It has 46 clinics, contracts with and/or uses 56 area hospitals and has just under 4,000 physicians.

Date Survey was Created: 1987.

Overview of Survey: Survey asks 36 questions, including qualifiers, open-ended, scaled and multiple-choice. Questions are arranged generally to match flow of subscribers' experiences with the plan. Survey includes questions seeking comparison with previous plan, plan strengths and opportunities for improvement, satisfaction in general and with specifics, switching intent and change in plan performance demographics.

Survey Used to Measure Patient Satisfaction With:

- Quality of medical care received from doctors, hospitals and other providers;
- Customer services;
- Costs of care;
- Access to care;
- Coverage;
- Simplicity of educational and other materials;
- Simplicity of paperwork;
- Likelihood of switching;
- Comparisons with previous plan.

Type of Patient Completing Survey: Sample of subscribers stratified by provider system.

When do Patients/Enrollees Complete Survey?: Fall of each year.

Background Information Collected on Those Completing the Survey: Demographic, including age, education, marital status, children, employer's insurance share, employment status, income, race and gender.

How are Survey Findings Used?: To identify plan strengths and opportunities for improvement. To identify areas for further research and action plans.

Date of Last Revision to Survey: 1994.

Purchase Price of Survey: Not for sale.

Contact Information: Dennis R. Casselberry, Health Alliance Plan of Michigan, 2850 West Grand Boulevard, Detroit, Mich. 48202, (313) 874-8321; fax (313) 874-7479.

13. Here are several things that could be used to rate health care plans. For each one please tell me whether HAP is better, about the same or worse than your previous health care plan. (IF "NO PREVIOUS PLAN" ASK ABOUT "OTHER HEALTH CARE PLANS YOU ARE FAMILIAR WITH")

(ROTATE)	Better	About the Same	Worse	DK	REF
( ) Number of medical services covered	1	2	3	8	9
( ) Cost	1	2	3	8	9
( ) Office hours	1	2	3	8	9
( ) Emergency care	1	2	3	8	9
( ) Personal attention	1	2	3	8	9
( ) Getting an appointment when you need it	1	2	3	8	9
( ) Many health care services at one location	1	2	3	8	9
( ) Quality of care	1	2	3	8	9

14. If you have a choice, how likely are you to switch to another health care plan? Are you...

    CONTINUE-------------|Very likely
                        |Somewhat likely

    SKIP TO Q.16----------|Only slightly likely
                         |Not at all likely
                         |Don't know
                         |Refused/NA

Healthcare Communications Systems

Kenner, La.

Title of Survey: No formal title. Firm performs various satisfaction data gathering tasks for hospitals and physician networks nationwide.

Profile of Organization: Healthcare Communications Systems is a consulting firm that provides management tools and services to various health care providers.

Date Survey was Created: N/A

Overview of Survey: Surveys examine three aspects of satisfactions:

- Performance functions, such as emergency room admission, regular admission, discharge, housekeeping, meals and meal service, nursing, nursing assistants, lab technicians, X-ray technicians, ancillary contact, ancillary performance and room and surroundings.

- Unit-by-unit analysis. Each discharge unit is examined according to 52 criteria. In-depth statistical analysis includes shift data and mentions of outstanding nurses and aides.

- Market factors, such as physician loyalty, patient loyalty, patient familiarity, managed care incidence, medical reputation, non-clinical reputation, patient satisfaction, word-of-mouth incidence, advertising and publicity and location and convenience.

Survey Used to Measure Patient Satisfaction With: See above.

Type of Patient Completing Survey: N/A

When do Patients/Enrollees Complete Survey?: N/A

Background Information Collected on Those Completing the Survey: Demographic.

How are Survey Findings Used?: To provide benchmark comparisons of satisfaction levels concerning acute inpatients, rehab inpatients, psychiatric inpatients, emergency room outpatients, same-day surgery outpatients, radiology outpatients, HMO members, and physician practices.

Date of Last Revision to Survey: N/A

Purchase Price of Survey: N/A

Contact Information: Healthcare Communication Systems, P.O. Box 219, Kenner, La. 70063, (504) 467-6435; fax (504) 467-6435.

Health Outcomes Institute

Bloomington, Minn.

Title of Survey: Satisfaction Survey

Profile of Organization: The Health Outcomes Institute works with researchers, clinicians, professional organizations and government agencies to develop and distribute public domain outcomes instruments and protocols.

Date Survey was Created: 1995.

Overview of Survey: Survey consists of a core set of 12 questions with some rotating questions.

Survey Used to Measure Patient Satisfaction With:

■ Quality of medical care received from doctors and other providers;

■ Customer services;

■ Access to care;

■ Participatory care;

■ Patient-centered care.

Type of Patient Completing Survey: All patients and care givers.

When do Patients/Enrollees Complete Survey?: After visiting a physician or physician extender.

Background Information Collected on Those Completing the Survey: Health status and demographic.

How are Survey Findings Used?: CQI and purchasing.

Date of Last Revision to Survey: 1996.

Purchase Price of Survey: N/A

Contact Information: David M. Radosevich, Ph.D., RN, Health Outcomes Institute, 2001 Killebrew Drive, Suite 122, Bloomington, Minn. 55424, (612) 858-9188; fax (612) 858-9189; e-mail davidmr@maroon.tc.umn.edu

Kaiser Foundation Health Plan of North Carolina

Raleigh, NC

Title of Survey: Patient Satisfaction Survey

Profile of Organization: Kaiser Foundation Health Plan of North Carolina, a part of the Kaiser network, serves 123,000 enrollees in parts of North Carolina and South Carolina.

Date Survey was Created: May 1991.

Overview of Survey: Currently in the process of redesigning survey. Expect to have between 15 and 25 questions asking overall satisfaction questions, satisfaction with wait times and staff members.

Survey Used to Measure Patient Satisfaction With:

- Quality of medical care received from doctors, health plan and other providers;
- Customer services;
- Access to care.

Type of Patient Completing Survey: Randomly selected patients who have had a recent outpatient visit at one of plan's medical facilities.

When do Patients/Enrollees Complete Survey?: Within one to three weeks after outpatient visit.

Background Information Collected on Those Completing the Survey: None.

How are Survey Findings Used?: Track patients' satisfaction with performance and services, which helps Kaiser focus on improvement activities.

Date of Last Revision to Survey: Current. New survey should be in effect by May 1996.

Purchase Price of Survey: N/A

Contact Information: Debbie Glackin, Kaiser Foundation Health Plan of North Carolina, 3120 Highwoods Boulevard, Raleigh, N.C. 27604-1038, (919) 981-6000; fax (919) 981-6052.

Kaiser Permanente Medical Group (Northern California Regional Office)

Oakland, Calif.

Title of Survey: Kaiser Permanente (Northern California Region) Patient Survey

Profile of Organization: The Northern California Regional Office of Kaiser Permanente Medical Group is an HMO serving 2,521,000 enrollees.

Date Survey was Created: 1994.

Overview of Survey: Eighty questions on the following categories:

- General;
- Access to care;
- Phones;
- Appointments;
- "Keeping you healthy";
- Physician interaction;
- Satisfaction;
- Demographic.

Survey Used to Measure Patient Satisfaction With: See above.

Type of Patient Completing Survey: Patient Survey is sent annually to 10% sample of patients who visit plan. **Member Survey** is sent to random sample yearly.

When do Patients/Enrollees Complete Survey?: Patient Survey is sent to patients approximately one month after office visit. **Member Survey** is sent to members annually.

Background Information Collected on Those Completing the Survey: Demographic.

How are Survey Findings Used?: To improve care and access to services. Results serve as a baseline against which future improvements can be measured.

Date of Last Revision to Survey: 1995.

Purchase Price of Survey: Not for sale.

Contact Information: Michael S. Ralston, M.D., Kaiser Permanente Medical Group (Northern California Region), 1950 Franklin Street, Oakland, Calif. 94612, (510) 987-3962; fax (510) 873-5099.

Please use the enclosed envelope and mail the completed survey to:
KAISER PERMANENTE, MEMBER AND PATIENT SURVEYS
1033 O ST. STE 401
LINCOLN, NE 68508-9855

MARKING INSTRUCTIONS	CORRECT MARK ○○●○	INCORRECT MARKS
	▪ Please use a pen or pencil	▪ Erase cleanly any marks you wish to change
	▪ Fill the circle completely	▪ Do not make any stray marks on this form

Thinking of your experiences in the past 12 months, how would you rate Kaiser Permanente on providing you with:

		Poor	Fair	Good	Very Good	Excellent	Not Applicable
1.	Quality health care	○	○	○	○	○	○
2.	Personal and responsive service	○	○	○	○	○	○
3.	Convenient and easy access	○	○	○	○	○	○

Thinking of your experiences with Kaiser Permanente in the past 12 months, please rate each of the following aspects of our care and service:

GENERAL

		Poor	Fair	Good	Very Good	Excellent	Not Applicable
4.	Your overall experience at Kaiser Permanente	○	○	○	○	○	○
5.	Respect shown for your time	○	○	○	○	○	○
6.	Courtesy and helpfulness of staff	○	○	○	○	○	○
7.	Caring attitude of staff	○	○	○	○	○	○
8.	Caring attitude of the physicians or other health care providers	○	○	○	○	○	○
9.	Coordination among all the people who care for you	○	○	○	○	○	○
10.	How well Kaiser Permanente follows up with you after you have a medical problem	○	○	○	○	○	○
11.	Manner in which you are informed of test results	○	○	○	○	○	○
12.	Extent to which physicians or other health care providers involve you in your medical decisions	○	○	○	○	○	○

Amount of time:

		Poor	Fair	Good	Very Good	Excellent	Not Applicable
13.	It takes for physicians, other health care providers, or staff to respond to your phone calls	○	○	○	○	○	○
14.	You have to wait at the medical facility when you have a scheduled appointment	○	○	○	○	○	○
15.	Physicians or other health care providers usually spend with you	○	○	○	○	○	○

ACCESS TO CARE

		Poor	Fair	Good	Very Good	Excellent	Not Applicable
16.	Ease of selecting a personal physician of your choice	○	○	○	○	○	○
17.	Information provided to assist you in selecting a personal physician	○	○	○	○	○	○

Ability to:

		Poor	Fair	Good	Very Good	Excellent	Not Applicable
18.	See a physician or other health care provider when you need to	○	○	○	○	○	○
19.	See the particular physician or other health care provider you want to see	○	○	○	○	○	○
20.	See your personal physician	○	○	○	○	○	○
21.	See a specialist when you need to	○	○	○	○	○	○
22.	Be referred to a specialist	○	○	○	○	○	○
23.	Be seen by a specialist once you are referred	○	○	○	○	○	○
24.	Get emergency care	○	○	○	○	○	○
25.	Get care in the evening	○	○	○	○	○	○
26.	Get care on the weekend	○	○	○	○	○	○

PHONES

		Poor	Fair	Good	Very Good	Excellent	Not Applicable
27.	Amount of time you have to wait on the phone before talking to someone	○	○	○	○	○	○
28.	Courtesy and helpfulness of telephone staff	○	○	○	○	○	○
29.	Helpfulness of phone advice received	○	○	○	○	○	○

Ability to:

		Poor	Fair	Good	Very Good	Excellent	Not Applicable
30.	Get through to the person who can solve your problem when you call	○	○	○	○	○	○
31.	Get through on the phone at a convenient time	○	○	○	○	○	○
32.	Get phone advice when you need it	○	○	○	○	○	○
33.	Get phone advice early in the morning	○	○	○	○	○	○
34.	Get phone advice at night	○	○	○	○	○	○
35.	Get phone advice on the weekend	○	○	○	○	○	○

APPOINTMENTS

36. Ability to get an appointment if you think you need one
37. Ability to get an appointment at a convenient time or on a convenient day

Amount of time you have to wait for:

38. An appointment for a serious or sudden medical problem, such as an ear infection, high fever, or vomiting
39. An appointment for a minor illness or pain, such as minor back pain, persistent fatigue, or minor skin problems
40. An appointment when you are not ill, but want to have a test such as an eye exam, a cholesterol check, or a Pap smear
41. A return appointment for follow-up on a <u>known</u> or existing condition such as pneumonia, diabetes, or hypertension
42. Any appointment

KEEPING YOU HEALTHY

43. How well Kaiser Permanente teaches you to care for common problems such as a cold or a sprained ankle
44. Ability to get advice and services to help you stay healthy
45. Your confidence in knowing when to see a health care professional as opposed to treating a medical problem yourself
46. How well Kaiser Permanente informs you when you should have preventive tests
47. Ability to get preventive tests when advised
48. Ability to get advice on specific actions you can take to stay healthy (such as stopping smoking)

R9862-PFI-5432

PLEASE DO NOT WRITE IN THIS AREA – FOR OFFICE USE ONLY – 239673

Thinking <u>specifically</u> about your appointment with Dr. Smith on May 22, 1995 in the Medicine department please rate the following aspects of our care and service:

	Poor	Fair	Good	Very Good	Excellent	Not Applicable
Amount of time you had to wait:						
49. For your appointment						
50. To register once you arrived at the medical facility						
51. In the waiting room						
52. In the exam room						

53. Extent to which you were kept informed about the reasons for any wait you experienced
54. Courtesy and helpfulness of staff
55. Caring attitude of staff
56. How familiar Dr. Smith was with your medical history
57. How easy Dr. Smith was to talk to
58. How well Dr. Smith listened and acknowledged your concerns

59. Courtesy and respect with which Dr. Smith treated you
60. Extent to which Dr. Smith explained what was being done in terms you could understand
61. Dr. Smith's skills and abilities
62. Caring attitude of Dr. Smith
63. Amount of time Dr. Smith spent with you
64. Extent to which Dr. Smith involved you in your medical decisions
65. Extent to which your questions had been answered by the time you left your appointment

66. All things considered, how satisfied are you with Kaiser Permanente?

Completely satisfied, couldn't be better	Very satisfied	Somewhat satisfied	Neither satisfied nor dissatisfied	Somewhat dissatisfied	Very dissatisfied	Completely dissatisfied, couldn't be worse

67. What was the main purpose of your visit? *(Please fill in only one selection)*
    ○ Preventive care   ○ Routine care   ○ Continuing care   ○ Urgent care   ○ Emergency care

68. Was this visit due to a job-related injury or illness?
    ○ Yes   ○ No   ○ Uncertain   ○ Not applicable

Please answer the following questions so we may compare your answers with others who respond to our survey:

69. Are you the Kaiser Permanente member to whom this survey was addressed?
- ○ Yes
- ○ No

70. Do your children have their own personal pediatrician at Kaiser Permanente, that is, one that they see for most of their routine care?
- ○ Yes
- ○ No
- ○ I have no children who are members of Kaiser Permanente

71. Do you have your own personal physician at Kaiser Permanente, that is, one that you see for most of your routine care?
- ○ Yes ○
- ○ No

72. What is your age?
- ○ Under 18 years
- ○ 18 - 34 years
- ○ 35 - 44 years
- ○ 45 - 64 years
- ○ 65 or over

73. What is your gender?
- ○ Male
- ○ Female

74. What is the highest grade you have completed in school?
- ○ Less than 12th grade
- ○ High school graduate
- ○ Some college/business/ technical school
- ○ College graduate
- ○ Graduate school

75. Which of the following best describes your ethnic background?
- ○ American Indian ○ Chinese
- ○ Black/African- American ○ Filipino
- ○ Japanese
- ○ Hispanic/Latino ○ Other Asian
- ○ White/Caucasian ○ Other

76. Have you been hospitalized in the last year?
- ○ Yes
- ○ No

77. How long have you been a Kaiser Permanente member?
- ○ Less than 1 year ○ 6 - 10 years
- ○ 1 - 2 years ○ 11 years or
- ○ 3 - 5 years more

78. How many visits have you made to any Kaiser Permanente provider in the last 12 months?
- ○ One ○ Four or five
- ○ Two or three ○ More than five

79. In general, would you say your health is:
- ○ Excellent
- ○ Very Good
- ○ Good
- ○ Fair
- ○ Poor

Do you have any comments about your last visit or your overall experiences with Kaiser Permanente? (Please do not write outside this shaded area - use a second sheet of paper if needed)

_____

Your opinion *will* make a difference. Thank you very much for your response.

© Copyright 1995 KFHP/KPMG

** 0207-D-0021 **

MR JOHN DOE
123 ANY STREET
ANYTOWN CA 90000-0000

FACILITY: OAK   DEPT: MED

Kaiser Member Survey

KAISER PERMANENTE

Kaiser Foundation Health Plan, Inc.
Northern California Region
1950 Franklin Street
Oakland, California 94612-2998

Please use the enclosed envelope and mail the completed survey to:
KAISER PERMANENTE, MEMBER AND PATIENT SURVEYS
1033 O ST. STE 401
LINCOLN, NE 68508-9855

Si usted desea una copia de esta
encuesta en Español llame sin costo
al teléfono: 1-800-733-6764

如果您對醫院服務有任何意見，請打
電話向我們索取一份中文意見調查卷。
1-800-733-6794

** 221096-X-XXXXX **

MR JOHN DOE
123 ANY STREET
ANYTOWN CA 12345-6789

Dear Mr. Doe:

At Kaiser Permanente, member satisfaction is one of our highest priorities. We are continually striving to improve the care and service we offer. As part of this effort, we are requesting your response to the enclosed survey regarding Kaiser Permanente.

Your participation in this survey is very important to us. The information provided by you and other members will be used by our physicians, managers, and staff for the following purposes:

- To identify ways to improve the care and service we provide to members
- To serve as a baseline against which future improvements in care and service can be measured

By completing the survey, you will help ensure that we receive the most complete picture of what you need and want.

You can be assured of complete confidentiality. Your name will not be associated with your individual responses and comments, as information from all participants will be combined and averaged. Your individual survey will be seen only by our Program Performance Assessment Department. If you have any questions about confidentiality, the purpose of the survey, or how to complete the survey, please call our Program Performance Assessment Department in Oakland at 1-800-777-1179.

Again, our focus is on our members, so your response is extremely important to us. We sincerely thank you for your participation.

David G. Pockell
Executive Vice President and Regional Manager
Kaiser Foundation Health Plan

Walter H. Caulfield, M.D.
Executive Director
The Permanente Medical Group

MARKING INSTRUCTIONS	CORRECT MARK ○ ○ ● ○	INCORRECT MARKS ⊘ ⊘ ⊘ ⦸
	▪ Please use a pen or pencil	▪ Erase cleanly any marks you wish to change
	▪ Fill the circle completely	▪ Do not make any stray marks on this form

Thinking of your _most recent_ experiences, how would you rate Kaiser Permanente on providing you with:

		Poor	Fair	Good	Very Good	Excellent	Not Applicable
1.	Quality health care	○	○	○	○	○	○
2.	Personal and responsive service	○	○	○	○	○	○
3.	Convenient and easy access	○	○	○	○	○	○

Thinking of your _most recent_ experiences with Kaiser Permanente, please rate each of the following aspects of our care and service:

GENERAL

		Poor	Fair	Good	Very Good	Excellent	Not Applicable
4.	Your overall experience at Kaiser Permanente	○	○	○	○	○	○
5.	Respect shown for your time	○	○	○	○	○	○
6.	Courtesy and helpfulness of staff	○	○	○	○	○	○
7.	Caring attitude of staff	○	○	○	○	○	○
8.	Caring attitude of the physicians or other health care providers	○	○	○	○	○	○
9.	Coordination among all the people who care for you	○	○	○	○	○	○
10.	How well Kaiser Permanente follows up with you after you have a medical problem	○	○	○	○	○	○
11.	Manner in which you are informed of test results	○	○	○	○	○	○
12.	Extent to which physicians or other health care providers involve you in your medical decisions	○	○	○	○	○	○

Amount of time:

		Poor	Fair	Good	Very Good	Excellent	Not Applicable
13.	It takes for physicians, other health care providers, or staff to respond to your phone calls	○	○	○	○	○	○
14.	You have to wait at the medical facility when you have a scheduled appointment	○	○	○	○	○	○
15.	Physicians or other health care providers usually spend with you	○	○	○	○	○	○

ACCESS TO CARE

		Poor	Fair	Good	Very Good	Excellent	Not Applicable
16.	Ease of selecting a personal physician of your choice	○	○	○	○	○	○
17.	Information provided to assist you in selecting a personal physician	○	○	○	○	○	○

Ability to:

		Poor	Fair	Good	Very Good	Excellent	Not Applicable
18.	See a physician or other health care provider when you need to	○	○	○	○	○	○
19.	See the _particular_ physician or other health care provider you want to see	○	○	○	○	○	○
20.	See your personal physician	○	○	○	○	○	○
21.	See a specialist when you need to	○	○	○	○	○	○
22.	Be referred to a specialist	○	○	○	○	○	○
23.	Be seen by a specialist once you are referred	○	○	○	○	○	○
24.	Get emergency care	○	○	○	○	○	○
25.	Get care in the evening	○	○	○	○	○	○
26.	Get care on the weekend	○	○	○	○	○	○

PHONES

		Poor	Fair	Good	Very Good	Excellent	Not Applicable
27.	Amount of time you have to wait on the phone before talking to someone	○	○	○	○	○	○
28.	Courtesy and helpfulness of telephone staff	○	○	○	○	○	○
29.	Helpfulness of phone advice received	○	○	○	○	○	○

FORM NO. H-102833-NRC -L   M2 1094 C C1560-12 11 10 9 8 7 6 5 4 3 2

PLEASE DO NOT WRITE IN THIS AREA – FOR OFFICE USE ONLY – 221096

PHONES (con't)

Ability to:

		Poor	Fair	Good	Very Good	Excellent	Not Applicable
30.	Get through to the person who can solve your problem when you call	○	○	○	○	○	○
31.	Get through on the phone at a convenient time	○	○	○	○	○	○
32.	Get phone advice when you need it	○	○	○	○	○	○
33.	Get phone advice early in the morning	○	○	○	○	○	○
34.	Get phone advice at night	○	○	○	○	○	○
35.	Get phone advice on the weekend	○	○	○	○	○	○

APPOINTMENTS

		Poor	Fair	Good	Very Good	Excellent	Not Applicable
36.	Ability to get an appointment if you think you need one	○	○	○	○	○	○
37.	Ability to get an appointment at a convenient time or on a convenient day	○	○	○	○	○	○

Amount of time you have to wait for:

		Poor	Fair	Good	Very Good	Excellent	Not Applicable
38.	An appointment for a serious or sudden medical problem, such as an ear infection, high fever, or vomiting	○	○	○	○	○	○
39.	An appointment for a minor illness or pain, such as minor back pain, persistent fatigue, or minor skin problems	○	○	○	○	○	○
40.	An appointment when you are not ill, but want to have a test such as an eye exam, a cholesterol check, or a Pap smear						
41.	A return appointment for follow-up on a known or existing condition such as pneumonia, diabetes, or hypertension	○	○	○	○	○	○
42.	Any appointment	○	○	○	○	○	○

KEEPING YOU HEALTHY

		Poor	Fair	Good	Very Good	Excellent	Not Applicable
43.	How well Kaiser Permanente teaches you to care for common problems such as a cold or a sprained ankle	○	○	○	○	○	○
44.	Ability to get advice and services to help you stay healthy	○	○	○	○	○	○
45.	Your confidence in knowing when to see a health care professional as opposed to treating a medical problem on your own	○	○	○	○	○	○
46.	How well Kaiser Permanente informs you when you should have preventive tests	○	○	○	○	○	○
47.	Ability to get preventive tests when advised	○	○	○	○	○	○
48.	Ability to get advice on specific actions you can take to stay healthy (such as stopping smoking)	○	○	○	○	○	○

49. All things considered, how satisfied are you with Kaiser Permanente?

Completely satisfied, couldn't be better	Very satisfied	Somewhat satisfied	Neither satisfied nor dissatisfied	Somewhat dissatisfied	Very dissatisfied	Completely dissatisfied, couldn't be worse
○	○	○	○	○	○	○

50. Do you have your own personal physician at Kaiser Permanente, that is, one that you see for most of your routine care?
○ Yes   ○ No   ○

51. Do your children have their own personal pediatrician at Kaiser Permanente, that is, one that they see for most of their routine care?
○ Yes   ○ No   ○ I have no children who are members of Kaiser Permanente

Please answer the following questions so we may compare your answers with others who respond to our survey:

52. Are you the Kaiser Permanente member to whom this survey was addressed?
○ Yes   ○ No

53. Have you been seen by a health care provider at a Kaiser Permanente facility in the last two months?
○ Yes   ○ No

54. Have you visited a Kaiser Permanente facility in the last twelve months?
○ Yes   ○ No
If yes, what was the main purpose of the visit? (Please fill in only one selection)
○ Accompany a family member or friend to a physician or therapist
○ Attend a class (such as stop smoking, exercise, stress management)
○ Physical or other therapy
○ Other: _____

55. What is your age?
○ Under 18 years   ○ 45 - 64 years
○ 18 - 34 years   ○ 65 or over
○ 35 - 44 years

56. Which of the following best describes your ethnic background?
○ American Indian   ○ Chinese
○ Black/African-American   ○ Filipino
○ Japanese
○ Hispanic/Latino   ○ Other Asian
○ White/Caucasian   ○ Other

57. What is the highest grade you have completed in school?
○ Less than 12th grade
○ High school graduate
○ Some college/business/technical school
○ College graduate
○ Graduate school

58. What is your gender?
○ Male
○ Female

59. How long have you been a Kaiser Permanente member?
○ Less than 1 year
○ 1 - 2 years
○ 3 - 5 years
○ 6 - 10 years
○ 11 years or more

60. In general, would you say your health is:
○ Excellent
○ Very Good
○ Good
○ Fair
○ Poor

If you were to need care at a Kaiser Permanente facility in the near future, which facility would you visit? (Please fill in only one selection)

○ Antioch	○ Hayward	○ Novato	○ Rancho Cordova	○ San Francisco	○ South Sacramento
○ Davis	○ Martinez	○ Oakland	○ Redwood City	○ San Rafael	○ South San Francisco
○ Fairfield	○ Milpitas	○ Park Shadelands	○ Richmond	○ Santa Clara	○ Stockton
○ Fremont	○ Mountain View	○ Petaluma	○ Roseville	○ Santa Rosa	○ Vallejo
○ Fresno	○ Napa	○ Pleasanton	○ Sacramento	○ Santa Teresa	○ Walnut Creek
○ Gilroy					

Do you have any comments about your overall experiences with Kaiser Permanente?
(Please do not write outside this shaded area - use a second sheet of paper if needed)

_____
_____
_____
_____

221096   MTN   © Copyright 1995 KPMP/TPMG   **Your opinion *will* make a difference. Thank you very much for your response.**

Maxicare Health Plans, Inc.

Los Angeles, Calif.

Title of Survey: Maxicare Member Satisfaction Survey

Profile of Organization: Maxicare Health Plans, Inc., is an IPA-model health plan serving about 119,000 members in California. It has 300 clinics, contracts with and/or uses 204 hospitals, and has over 13,000 physicians in the network.

Date Survey was Created: N/A

Overview of Survey: N/A

Survey Used to Measure Patient Satisfaction With:

- Quality of medical care received from doctors, health plans and hospitals;
- Customer services;
- Access to care;
- Simplicity of educational and other materials;
- Simplicity of paperwork.

Type of Patient Completing Survey: Random sampling of Maxicare membership.

When do Patients/Enrollees Complete Survey?: Survey is sent to patients annually each Spring.

Background Information Collected on Those Completing the Survey: None.

How are Survey Findings Used?: To assess the satisfaction of Maxicare members in the areas listed above.

Date of Last Revision to Survey: N/A

Purchase Price of Survey: Not for sale.

Contact Information: Ed Coghlan, Maxicare Health Plans, Inc., 1149 South Broadway, Suite 923, Los Angeles, Calif. 90015, (213) 765-2112; fax (213) 765-2693.

MedSurv, Inc.

Granville, Ohio

Title of Survey: MedSurv Survey

Profile of Organization: MedSurv, Inc., is a patient satisfaction survey administrator focusing on evaluation, management services and procedures.

Date Survey was Created: 1995.

Overview of Survey: MedSurv performs two types of patient satisfaction surveys. Survey A, for use by managed care organizations, independent practice associations and physician hospital organizations, establishes the relative satisfaction patients express with physicians providing services for the organization. Survey B helps physicians directly assess their own practices. Both surveys result in the same comprehensive report containing an overview of patient satisfaction and a physician performance grade.

Survey Used to Measure Patient Satisfaction With: See above.

Type of Patient Completing Survey: Recent outpatient visit.

When do Patients/Enrollees Complete Survey?: N/A

Background Information Collected on Those Completing the Survey: None.

How are Survey Findings Used?: To track the quality of care provided by physicians and their staffs on an outpatient basis, then compare results to physicians in other geographic locations through a common numerical reference point.

Date of Last Revision to Survey: 1995.

Purchase Price of Survey: Call for prices.

Contact Information: MedSurv, Inc., P.O. Box 456, Granville, Ohio 43023, (614) 587-0773; fax (614) 457-4052.

National Committee on Quality Assurance

Washington, D.C.

Title of Survey: The Annual Member Health Care Survey

Profile of Organization: The National Committee on Quality Assurance (NCQA) accredits, and develops quality standards for, managed care organizations.

Date Survey was Created: July 1995.

Overview of Survey: Survey consists of 75 questions in four major areas: enrollment and use of services; satisfaction with care and services; health and daily activities; socio-demographic status. Survey is designed to be administered by mail, by a third-party research organization.

Survey Used to Measure Patient Satisfaction With:

- Quality of medical care received from doctors, health plans and other providers;
- Customer services;
- Costs of care;
- Access to care;
- Coverage;
- Simplicity of paperwork;
- Patient health status;
- Availability of other materials on eligibility, covered services and administrative issues.

Type of Patient Completing Survey: Random sample of plan enrollees, regardless of whether or not services have been used.

When do Patients/Enrollees Complete Survey?: Annually.

Background Information Collected on Those Completing the Survey: None.

How are Survey Findings Used?: To support purchaser and consumer decisionmaking.

Date of Last Revision to Survey: July 1995.

Purchase Price of Survey: A manual is available for $50 that contains the instrument, the sampling and data collection protocol and information about the selection of items included in the survey.

Contact Information: Laura Aiuppa, Senior Health Care Analyst, National Committee for Quality Assurance, 2000 L Street, NW, Suite 500, Washington, D.C. 20009, (202) 955-3500; fax (202) 955-3599.

National Hospice Organization

Arlington, Va.

Title of Survey: Family Satisfaction Survey

Profile of Organization: The National Hospice Organization promotes the principles of the hospice concept and program of care for the terminally ill and their families among the general public and professionals.

Date Survey was Created: 1994.

Overview of Survey: Three "yes/no" questions; eight specific questions (Linkert scale); one open-ended suggestion area; one open-ended comments area.

Survey Used to Measure Patient Satisfaction With:

- Quality of symptom management from hospice team;
- Customer services;
- Access to care;
- Coverage;
- Simplicity of educational materials and other materials;
- Caregiver satisfaction with support provided to them, not just to patient.

Type of Patient Completing Survey: Survivors of recently deceased hospice patients complete survey.

When do Patients/Enrollees Complete Survey?: Survey is sent to survivors approximately two months after patient's death.

Background Information Collected on Those Completing the Survey: Demographic.

How are Survey Findings Used?: To benchmark outcome data.

Date of Last Revision to Survey: 1995.

Purchase Price of Survey: N/A

Contact Information: Susan Buckley or Chris Cody, National Hospice Organization, 1901 North Moore Street, Suite 901, Arlington, Va. 22209, (703) 243-5900; fax (703) 525-5762.

National Research Corporation

Lincoln, Neb.

Title of Survey: The NRC Listening System

Profile of Organization: National Research Corporation is a market research company specializing in the health care industry.

Date Survey was Created: N/A

Overview of Survey: Survey contains 25 to 30 questions from four categories: critical service factors; core encounter; health care organization system; facility/unit.

Survey Used to Measure Patient Satisfaction With:

- Quality of medical care received from doctors, health plans, hospitals and other providers;
- Customer services;
- Costs of care;
- Access to care;
- Coverage;
- Simplicity of educational and other materials;
- Simplicity of paperwork;
- Advocacy.

Type of Patient Completing Survey: Various surveys for health plan enrollees and hospital patients, physician office patients, outpatients, emergency room patients, home health patients, rehab patients and dental patients.

When do Patients/Enrollees Complete Survey?: Encounter-specific surveys are completed seven to 10 days after visit or discharge. Non-encounter-specific surveys (such as for health plan enrollees) vary.

Background Information Collected on Those Completing the Survey: Demographic.

How are Survey Findings Used?: They are tabulated into one-page action plans that report on trends from previous reporting periods, and make national and local market comparisons.

Date of Last Revision to Survey: Ongoing.

Purchase Price of Survey: Call for quote.

Contact Information: Kristine L. Benson, Director of Marketing, National Research Corporation, 1033 O Street, Gold's Galleria, Lincoln, Neb. 68508, (402) 475-2525; fax (402) 475-9061.

 MeritCare

** 220646-D-12345 **

MR JOHN DOE
123 ANY STREET
ANYTOWN CA 12345-6789

Dear Mr. Doe:

MeritCare Hospital is committed to improving the care and services our patients receive. As part of the improvement process, we are asking for your help to identify areas in need of improvement. Recently, you were a surgery patient of our hospital from May 1 through May 5. Please take a few minutes to answer a few questions about your stay. We are able to sample only a small number of patients, so your response is very important.

After you have completed this brief questionnaire, simply return it in the enclosed postage-paid envelope.

Your responses are confidential. Results are reviewed in summary form with answers from many other patients.

Thank you for your help.

Lloyd V. Smith, CEO/President
MeritCare Hospital

MARKING INSTRUCTIONS	INCORRECT MARKS ⊘⊗◯⦸	CORRECT MARK ◯◯●◯
	■ Please use a pen or pencil	■ Erase cleanly any marks you wish to change
	■ Fill the circle completely	■ Do not make any stray marks on this form

Mr. Doe, how would you rate MeritCare Hospital on the:	Poor	Fair	Good	Very Good	Excellent
1. Overall quality of care and service you received	◯	◯	◯	◯	◯
2. Clear and complete explanation provided by the staff about your tests and procedures	◯	◯	◯	◯	◯
3. Thoroughness of examinations	◯	◯	◯	◯	◯
4. How well the nurses and staff listened to you	◯	◯	◯	◯	◯
5. Sensitivity of the nurses and staff to your needs as an individual and as a patient	◯	◯	◯	◯	◯
6. Skill and experience of the nurses and staff providing treatment for you	◯	◯	◯	◯	◯
7. How quickly the nurses and staff responded to you	◯	◯	◯	◯	◯
8. Clear and complete explanation provided by the nurses and staff about your daily routine	◯	◯	◯	◯	◯
9. The communication provided by the nurses and staff to your family	◯	◯	◯	◯	◯
10. Courtesy and respect shown to you by the nurses and staff	◯	◯	◯	◯	◯
11. The outcome of your medical care, how much you were helped	◯	◯	◯	◯	◯

12. Have you called or written with a complaint or problem?   ◯ Yes   ◯ No   (If no, go to question 14)

	Poor	Fair	Good	Very Good	Excellent
13. How would you rate the time it took to resolve the complaint or problem?	◯	◯	◯	◯	◯

PLEASE DO NOT WRITE IN THIS AREA - FOR OFFICE USE ONLY -- 220646

	Definitely Would Not	Probably Would Not	Might or Might Not	Probably Would	Definitely Would
14. Would you recommend MeritCare Hospital to family and friends?	○	○	○	○	○

Mr. Doe, how would you rate MeritCare Hospital on the:

	Poor	Fair	Good	Very Good	Excellent
15. Quality of nursing care	○	○	○	○	○
16. Promptness and efficiency of the admission process	○	○	○	○	○
17. Clear and complete explanation of the visiting hours during admission	○	○	○	○	○
18. Responsiveness of the staff when you called	○	○	○	○	○
19. Kindness and caring of your doctor	○	○	○	○	○
20. Frequency of the staff checking on you to see if you needed anything	○	○	○	○	○
21. Temperature of the food when it was served	○	○	○	○	○
22. Clear and complete explanation provided about your diet	○	○	○	○	○
23. Cleanliness of your room	○	○	○	○	○
24. Clear and complete explanation of the billing procedures	○	○	○	○	○

	Excellent	Very Good	Good	Fair	Poor
25. Would you say your health is:	○	○	○	○	○

ADDITIONAL COMMENTS IN REGARD TO YOUR HOSPITAL STAY: (Use a second sheet of paper if necessary)

26. If you would like to be contacted by MeritCare Hospital, please darken this oval: ○

Your opinion will make a difference. Thank you very much for your response.

V1

Alpha Medical Clinic

** 220646-D-12345 **

MR ALLEN THOMPSON
123 ANY STREET
ANYTOWN CA 12345-6789

Dear Mr. Thompson:

Together, Alpha Medical Clinic and Dr. Anderson, your primary care physician, need your feedback to continually improve the services you receive. After you have completed this brief questionnaire, please insert it into the enclosed postage paid return envelope and drop it in the mail.

Your responses are confidential. Results are reviewed in summary form with answers from many other individuals.

Thank you for your help.

John B. Smith
President, Alpha Medical Clinic

MARKING INSTRUCTIONS	INCORRECT MARKS ⊘⊗○⊘	CORRECT MARK ○○●○
	• Please use a pen or pencil	• Erase cleanly any marks you wish to change
	• Fill the circle completely	• Do not make any stray marks on this form

1. All things considered, how satisfied are you with Alpha Medical Clinic?

Completely satisfied, couldn't be better	Very satisfied	Somewhat satisfied	Neither satisfied nor dissatisfied	Somewhat dissatisfied	Very dissatisfied	Completely dissatisfied, couldn't be worse
○	○	○	○	○	○	○

Mr. Thompson, how would you rate Alpha Medical Clinic on the:

	Poor	Fair	Good	Very Good	Excellent
2. Ease of seeing the doctor you were referred to	○	○	○	○	○
3. Length of time spent filling out claim forms or other paperwork	○	○	○	○	○
4. Amount <u>you</u> pay **out of pocket** (for example, co-payments, deductibles, payments for services not covered)	○	○	○	○	○
5. Access to medical care whenever you need it, even after hours	○	○	○	○	○

6. Would you recommend Alpha Medical Clinic to your family or friends if they needed care?

Definitely would not	Probably would not	Not sure	Probably would	Definitely would
○	○	○	○	○

7. What was the main purpose of your most recent visit with Dr. Anderson? **(darken only <u>ONE</u> oval)**
○ Physical Exam or Check-up   ○ Emergency or Urgent Care
○ Chronic or On-going Condition

8. How many days were between the day the appointment was made and the day you saw Dr. Anderson?
   ○ Same day   ○ 1 - 2 days   ○ 3 - 7 days
   ○ 8 - 14 days   ○ 15 - 30 days   ○ More than 30 days

9. How many minutes did it take to drive/reach Dr. Anderson's office?
   ○ 5 minutes or less   ○ 6 - 15 minutes   ○ 16 - 25 minutes   ○ More than 25 minutes

10. How many minutes did you spend waiting past the appointment time to see Dr. Anderson?
    ○ Did not wait   ○ 1 - 10 minutes   ○ 11 - 20 minutes   ○ 21 - 30 minutes   ○ More than 30 minutes

Mr. Thompson, thinking about your visit to Dr. Anderson, how would you rate:

	Poor	Fair	Good	Very Good	Excellent
11. Overall quality of care and services received from Dr. Anderson	○	○	○	○	○
12. Thoroughness of examinations and accuracy of diagnoses	○	○	○	○	○
13. Explanations of medical procedures and tests	○	○	○	○	○
14. Personal interest in you and your medical problems	○	○	○	○	○
15. Friendliness and courtesy shown to you by Dr. Anderson's staff	○	○	○	○	○
16. The outcomes of your medical care, how much you are helped	○	○	○	○	○
17. Advice you get about ways to avoid illness and stay healthy	○	○	○	○	○
18. The amount of time you have with Dr. Anderson and staff during a visit	○	○	○	○	○

	Definitely would not	Probably would not	Not sure	Probably would	Definitely would
19. Would you recommend Dr. Anderson to your family or friends?	○	○	○	○	○

20. Have you called or written Alpha Medical Clinic with a complaint or problem in the **past 12 months**?
    ○ Yes   ○ No (skip to question 22)

21. How many days did it take for Alpha Medical Clinic to resolve your complaint or problem?
    ○ Same day   ○ 1 - 5 days   ○ 6 - 10 days   ○ 11 - 14 days   ○ More than 14 days   ○ Not yet resolved

	Excellent	Very Good	Good	Fair	Poor
22. In general, would you say your health is:	○	○	○	○	○

Do you have any comments about your last visit or your overall experiences with Alpha Medical Clinic?
(Please do not write outside this area - use a second sheet of paper if needed)

_____
_____
_____
_____
_____
_____
_____

If you would like to be contacted by an Alpha Medical Clinic representative, please darken this oval: ○

National Research Corporation, Lincoln, NE
1-800-338-4264

NCG Research, Inc.

Nashville, Tenn.

Title of Survey: Your Hospital Stay: The Patient's Viewpoint

Profile of Organization: NCG Research, Inc. conducts patient satisfaction research for hospitals and physicians.

Date Survey was Created: 1989.

Overview of Survey: There are a total of 110 questions about patient satisfaction and health status collected by mail survey four to 12 weeks post-discharge. The data collection is carefully controlled, including follow-up, and averages a 60% response rate. The questionnaire data is merged with extensive patient file data from the hospital, such as UB92, clinical pathways and discharge unit.

Survey Used to Measure Patient Satisfaction With:

- Quality of medical care received from doctors, health plans and hospitals;
- Customer services;
- Costs of care;
- Access to care;
- Coverage;
- Simplicity of educational and other materials;
- Simplicity of paperwork.

Type of Patient Completing Survey: All inpatient discharges except those discharged against medical advice.

When do Patients/Enrollees Complete Survey?: Four to 12 weeks post-discharge.

Background Information Collected on Those Completing the Survey: N/A

How are Survey Findings Used?: Organizations use the survey for internal process improvement, to satisfy Joint Commission and NCQA requirements, in managed care contract negotiations, to set performance specifications for certain vendor contracts (such as food service), and in facility and strategic market planning.

Date of Last Revision to Survey: Ongoing.

Purchase Price of Survey: Contact NCG Research, Inc. for prices.

Contact Information: Barbara J. McEwen, Sales Manager, NCG Research, Inc., 1321 Murfreesboro Road, Suite 210, P.O. Box 292169, Nashville, Tenn. 37229-2169, (615) 399-0408; fax (615) 399-0608; e-mail bmcewen@ncgresearch.com

*Your
Hospital Stay:
The Patient's
Viewpoint*

Please answer this questionnaire for your most recent stay in our hospital. For each question, "X" one box that best answers the question.

BACKGROUND ON YOUR HOSPITAL STAY

1. Before this hospitalization, about how many times have you been admitted to this same hospital and stayed one or more nights?
   - ☐₁ Never, this was the first time ever
   - ☐₂ One other time
   - ☐₃ Two other times
   - ☐₄ Three or more other times

2. Have you ever been treated before at this hospital as an outpatient or an emergency room patient?
   - ☐₁ Yes
   - ☐₂ No

3. Thinking about your recent hospitalization, who chose this hospital? ("X" ALL THAT APPLY. YOU MAY CHOOSE MORE THAN ONE.)
   - ☐₁ Doctor chose
   - ☐₂ Patient or family member chose
   - ☐₃ Someone else chose
   - ☐₄ My insurance/health plan requires it
   - ☐₅ My insurance/health plan encourages it

4. Were you admitted to the hospital . . .
   - ☐₁ Through the Emergency Room
   - ☐₂ Through the Admitting Office
   - ☐₃ Other (SPECIFY):_____
   - ☐₄ Transferred from another institution

5. The time it took to get you settled in your room was . . .
   - ☐₅ Excellent
   - ☐₄ Very Good
   - ☐₃ Good
   - ☐₂ Fair
   - ☐₁ Poor

♻ recycled paper

Q-H912 12/12/94

60

6. For *most* of your stay, were you . . .
   - ☐₁ Alone in a private room
   - ☐₂ Alone in a semi-private room
   - ☐₃ In a room with other patient(s)

7. For *most* of your stay, were you on a special diet or could you eat regular foods?
   - ☐₁ Regular or unrestricted diet
   - ☐₂ Liquid diet
   - ☐₃ Special diet (other than liquid)
   - ☐₄ Don't know

8. During your hospital stay, how much help did you need with your everyday activities (eating, bathing, dressing, using the bathroom, getting out of bed)? Did you need . . .
   - ☐₁ A lot of help
   - ☐₂ Quite a bit of help
   - ☐₃ Some help
   - ☐₄ Little help
   - ☐₅ Never needed help

9. During your hospital stay, how much pain did you experience?
   - ☐₁ A lot of pain
   - ☐₂ Quite a bit of pain
   - ☐₃ Some pain
   - ☐₄ A little pain
   - ☐₅ No pain at all

10. Do you think that the amount of time you spent in the hospital was . . .
    - ☐₁ About right
    - ☐₂ Too short
    - ☐₃ Too long
    - ☐₄ Not sure

11. Where did you (the patient) stay in the hospital? In a section of the hospital for . . . ("X" ALL THAT APPLY. YOU MAY CHOOSE MORE THAN ONE.)
    - ☐₁ Adult surgery
    - ☐₂ Adult non-surgery
    - ☐₃ Heart/Coronary Care
    - ☐₄ Intensive/Critical Care
    - ☐₅ Childbirth/Maternity
    - ☐₆ Children/Pediatrics (not newborns)
    - ☐₇ Other
    - ☐₈ Can't recall type of unit

NCG Research, Inc.

Nashville, Tenn.

Title of Survey: Your Outpatient Surgery: The Patient's Viewpoint

Profile of Organization: NCG Research, Inc. conducts patient satisfaction research for hospitals and physicians.

Date Survey was Created: 1992.

Overview of Survey: N/A

Survey Used to Measure Patient Satisfaction With:

- Quality of medical care received from doctors, health plans and hospitals;
- Customer services;
- Costs of care;
- Access to care;
- Coverage;
- Simplicity of educational and other materials;
- Simplicity of paperwork.

Type of Patient Completing Survey: Outpatient surgery patients.

When do Patients/Enrollees Complete Survey?: N/A

Background Information Collected on Those Completing the Survey: N/A

How are Survey Findings Used?: Organizations use the survey for internal process improvement, to satisfy Joint Commission and NCQA requirements, in managed care contract negotiations, to set performance specifications for certain vendor contracts (such as food service), and in facility and strategic market planning.

Date of Last Revision to Survey: Ongoing.

Purchase Price of Survey: Contact NCG Research, Inc. for prices.

Contact Information: Barbara J. McEwen, Sales Manager, NCG Research, Inc., 1321 Murfreesboro Road, Suite 210, P.O. Box 292169, Nashville, Tenn. 37229-2169, (615) 399-0408; fax (615) 399-0608; e-mail bmcewen@ncgresearch.com

Your Outpatient Surgery:
The Patient's Viewpoint

Please answer this questionnaire as it relates to your outpatient surgery on the date noted in the attached letter. For each question, check (x) the box that best answers the question.

BACKGROUND ON YOUR HOSPITAL VISIT

1. Please record the date of your **outpatient surgery** that is mentioned in the attached letter.
   _____/_____/_____
   (Month   -   Day   -   Year)

2. Which of the following best describes your general health when you were admitted to the hospital?

   ❑5 Excellent
   ❑4 Very Good
   ❑3 Good
   ❑2 Fair
   ❑1 Poor

3. Have you ever been treated at this hospital as an inpatient or emergency room patient?

   ❑1 Yes   ❑2 No

4. Which of the following best describes the reason for your recent visit to our outpatient surgery department? Was it...?

   ❑20 Surgery that required an overnight stay
   ❑21 Surgery that did not require an overnight stay
   ❑99 Don't know

5. Thinking about your recent outpatient surgery, who chose this hospital?
   [CHECK ALL THAT APPLY]

   ❑1 Doctor chose
   ❑2 Patient or family member chose
   ❑3 Someone else chose
   ❑4 My insurance/health plan requires it
   ❑5 My insurance/health plan encourages it
   ❑6 Other (Specify):_____

Q-S900-5/9/94

6. Was the entire amount of time you spent at the hospital for your surgery...

❏1 Less than 5 hours
❏2 5 to 8 hours
❏3 9 to 12 hours
❏4 13 to 16 hours
❏5 17 to 20 hours
❏6 21 to 24 hours
❏7 More than 24 hours

7. At what time of day did you come to the hospital for your surgery?

❏1 Between 7:00 a.m. and 11:00 a.m.
❏2 Between 11:00 a.m. and 3:00 p.m.
❏3 Between 3:00 p.m. and 7:00 p.m.
❏4 Between 7:00 p.m. and 11:00 p.m.
❏5 Between 11:00 p.m. and 3:00 a.m.
❏6 Between 3:00 a.m. and 7:00 a.m.

8. On what day of the week was your surgery? [CHECK ONE]

❏1 Monday
❏2 Tuesday
❏3 Wednesday
❏4 Thursday
❏5 Friday
❏6 Saturday
❏7 Sunday

9. Do you think the amount of time you spent at the hospital for your outpatient surgery was....

❏1 About right
❏2 Too short
❏3 Too long
❏4 Not sure

GETTING TO THE HOSPITAL

	Excellent	Very Good	Good	Fair	Poor	Doesn't Apply
10. LOCATION: The convenience of this hospital's location for you	❏5	❏4	❏3	❏2	❏1	❏9
11. SIGNS TO THE HOSPITAL: Clarity and number of signs that direct you to the hospital	❏5	❏4	❏3	❏2	❏1	❏9
12. PARKING: Number of spaces available, convenience of location and cost	❏5	❏4	❏3	❏2	❏1	❏9
13. SIGNS AND DIRECTIONS: Ease of finding your way around the hospital	❏5	❏4	❏3	❏2	❏1	❏9
14. HOSPITAL BUILDING: How you would rate the hospital building overall	❏5	❏4	❏3	❏2	❏1	❏9

PRE-ADMISSIONS TESTING/INTERVIEW
(Before the day you came for surgery)

	Excellent	Very Good	Good	Fair	Poor	Doesn't Apply
15. WAITING TIME: The amount of time you had to wait for pre-admission testing/interview	❏5	❏4	❏3	❏2	❏1	❏9
16. PERSONAL MANNER: The respect, friendliness and courtesy shown by the pre-admission staff	❏5	❏4	❏3	❏2	❏1	❏9
17. PREPARATION FOR ADMISSION: How clear and complete was the information about how to prepare for your stay in the hospital	❏5	❏4	❏3	❏2	❏1	❏9

NCG Research, Inc.

Nashville, Tenn.

Title of Survey: Outpatient Tests and Treatment Survey

Profile of Organization: NCG Research, Inc. conducts patient satisfaction research for hospitals and physicians.

Date Survey was Created: 1992.

Overview of Survey: Phone survey.

Survey Used to Measure Patient Satisfaction With:

- Quality of medical care received from doctors, health plans and hospitals;
- Customer services;
- Costs of care;
- Access to care;
- Coverage;
- Simplicity of educational and other materials;
- Simplicity of paperwork.

Type of Patient Completing Survey: Hospital outpatients.

When do Patients/Enrollees Complete Survey?: N/A

Background Information Collected on Those Completing the Survey: N/A

How are Survey Findings Used?: Organizations use the survey for internal process improvement, to satisfy Joint Commission and NCQA requirements, in managed care contract negotiations, to set performance specifications for certain vendor contracts (such as food service), and in facility and strategic market planning.

Date of Last Revision to Survey: Ongoing.

Purchase Price of Survey: Contact NCG Research, Inc. for prices.

Contact Information: Barbara J. McEwen, Sales Manager, NCG Research, Inc., 1321 Murfreesboro Road, Suite 210, P.O. Box 292169, Nashville, Tenn. 37229-2169, (615) 399-0408; fax (615) 399-0608; e-mail bmcewen@ncgresearch.com

NCG Research
Nashville, TN 37203

Q-T900A-8/15/95

Phone No:_____

Time Began:_____

Interviewer Name:_____

Time Ended:_____

Interviewer ID:_____

Length:_____Minutes

Date:_____

Edit:_____

OUTPATIENT TESTS AND TREATMENT SURVEY

Hello, I'm _____ with NCG Research, a health care research firm. In an effort to monitor and improve services to outpatients, **[NAME OF HOSPITAL]** has asked us to call and find out what you think about your recent outpatient visit for **[TYPE FROM LABEL, INCLUDE DESCRIPTION IF NECESSARY]** . Your opinions are valuable and will be presented along with those of other outpatients. To maintain strict confidentiality, no one will be identified by name.

1) Did you visit as an outpatient for **[TYPE FROM LABEL]** on **[DATE]**?

[CONTINUE]	Yes	1
[CONTINUE]	No, different date or don't know date	2
	[SPECIFY: _____] (Mo-Day-Yr)	
[THANK AND TERMINATE]	Never	3
[THANK AND TERMINATE]	Don't Know if I was there	7
[THANK AND TERMINATE]	REF	9

2) How long did you have to wait to get this appointment? (How many days were there between the date you scheduled the appointment and the date of the appointment?)
[RECORD AMOUNT OF TIME] __ __ __ **DAYS**

[SKIP TO Q.4]	Doesn't Apply (Walk-in, etc.)	666
	DK	777
	REF	999

3) Do you think this length of time was ... **[READ LIST]**

	Excellent	5
	Very Good	4
	Good	3
	Fair	2
	Poor	1
[DO NOT READ]	DK	7
[DO NOT READ]	NA	8
[DO NOT READ]	REF	9

4) What was the entire amount of time you spent there for this visit?

__ __ . __ **HOURS**

DK	77.7
REF	99.9

66

NCG Research, Inc.
Nashville, Tenn.

Title of Survey: Emergency Department Survey

Profile of Organization: NCG Research, Inc. conducts patient satisfaction research for hospitals and physicians.

Date Survey was Created: 1992.

Overview of Survey: Phone survey conducted for individual hospitals.

Survey Used to Measure Patient Satisfaction With:

- Quality of medical care received from doctors, health plans and hospitals;
- Customer services;
- Costs of care;
- Access to care;
- Coverage;
- Simplicity of educational and other materials;
- Simplicity of paperwork.

Type of Patient Completing Survey: Hospital emergency room patients.

When do Patients/Enrollees Complete Survey?: N/A

Background Information Collected on Those Completing the Survey: N/A

How are Survey Findings Used?: Organizations use the survey for internal process improvement, to satisfy Joint Commission and NCQA requirements, in managed care contract negotiations, to set performance specifications for certain vendor contracts (such as food service), and in facility and strategic market planning.

Date of Last Revision to Survey: Ongoing.

Purchase Price of Survey: Contact NCG Research, Inc. for prices.

Contact Information: Barbara J. McEwen, Sales Manager, NCG Research, Inc., 1321 Murfreesboro Road, Suite 210, P.O. Box 292169, Nashville, Tenn. 37229-2169, (615) 399-0408; fax (615) 399-0608; e-mail bmcewen@ncgresearch.com

---

Phone No:_____

Time Began:_____

Interviewer Name:_____

Time Ended:_____

Interviewer ID:_____

Length:_____Minutes

Date:_____

Edit:_____

EMERGENCY DEPARTMENT SURVEY
_____ HOSPITAL

Hello, I'm _____ with NCG Research, a health care research firm. In an effort to monitor and improve services to emergency department patients, _____ hospital has asked us to call and find out what you think about your recent emergency department visit. Your opinions are valuable and will be presented along with those of other patients. To maintain strict confidentiality no one will be identified by name.

S1. Did you visit _____ Hospital as an emergency department on [DATE]?

[CONTINUE]	Yes	1
[CONTINUE]	No, different date or don't know date	2
	[SPECIFY: __-__-__] (M-D-Y)	
[THANK AND TERMINATE]	Never	3
[THANK AND TERMINATE]	Don't Know if I was there	7
[THANK AND TERMINATE]	REF	9

S2. Were you admitted to the hospital on the same day as this emergency department visit?

Yes	1
No	2
Don't Know	7
REF	9

1. Which of these categories best describes the nature of your visit to the emergency department?   [READ CATEGORIES]

Emergency Care: Immediate threat of life or limb that must be treated within minutes (such as a heart attack, massive bleeding, etc.) 1

Urgent Care: Potentially life-threatening situations that must be treated within 30 minutes to 2 hours (such as broken bones, abdominal pain, burns, eye infections, minor cuts, etc.) 2

Basic Care: Conditions that do not require immediate attention (such as rashes, flu, sore throat, etc.) 3

Don't Know	7
REF	9

Q-E900-1/10/95

NCG Research, Inc.

Nashville, Tenn.

Title of Survey: Your Home Health Care: The Patient's Viewpoint

Profile of Organization: NCG Research, Inc. conducts patient satisfaction research for hospitals and physicians.

Date Survey was Created: 1994.

Overview of Survey: N/A

Survey Used to Measure Patient Satisfaction With:

- Quality of medical care received from doctors, health plans, hospitals and other home health care providers;
- Customer services;
- Costs of care;
- Access to care;
- Coverage;
- Simplicity of educational and other materials;
- Simplicity of paperwork.

Type of Patient Completing Survey: Home health care patients.

When do Patients/Enrollees Complete Survey?: N/A

Background Information Collected on Those Completing the Survey: N/A

How are Survey Findings Used?: Organizations use the survey for internal process improvement, to satisfy Joint Commission and NCQA requirements, in managed care contract negotiations, to set performance specifications for certain vendor contracts (such as food service), and in facility and strategic market planning.

Date of Last Revision to Survey: Ongoing.

Purchase Price of Survey: Contact NCG Research, Inc. for prices.

Contact Information: Barbara J. McEwen, Sales Manager, NCG Research, Inc., 1321 Murfreesboro Road, Suite 210, P.O. Box 292169, Nashville, Tenn. 37229-2169, (615) 399-0408; fax (615) 399-0608; e-mail bmcewen@ncgresearch.com

Your Home Health Care:
The Patient's Viewpoint[SM]

Please let us know about your recent home health care experience by checking the box below which best answers each question.

SCHEDULING VISITS TO YOUR HOME

	Excellent	Very Good	Good	Fair	Poor	Doesn't Apply
1. BEING ON TIME: Coming to your home at the time we promised	□5	□4	□3	□2	□1	□6
2. PHONE COURTESY: Courtesy and respect shown to you over the phone	□5	□4	□3	□2	□1	□6

CONCERN FOR YOUR CARE

	Excellent	Very Good	Good	Fair	Poor	Doesn't Apply
3. CONSIDERATION OF YOUR NEEDS: Willingness of our staff to meet your needs	□5	□4	□3	□2	□1	□6

KEEPING YOU INFORMED

	Excellent	Very Good	Good	Fair	Poor	Doesn't Apply
4. EASE OF GETTING INFORMATION: Willingness of our staff to answer your questions	□5	□4	□3	□2	□1	□6
5. INSTRUCTIONS: How well we did in teaching you about your care, the equipment and how to care for yourself	□5	□4	□3	□2	□1	□6

YOUR MEDICAL CARE

	Excellent	Very Good	Good	Fair	Poor	Doesn't Apply
6. ATTENTION OF NURSES TO YOUR CONDITION: The amount of time the nurse spent with you	□5	□4	□3	□2	□1	□6
7. INFORMATION GIVEN BY NURSES: How well nurses communicated with patients, families and doctors	□5	□4	□3	□2	□1	□6

YOUR MEDICAL EQUIPMENT AND SUPPLIES

	Excellent	Very Good	Good	Fair	Poor	Doesn't Apply
8. PROMPTNESS: Delivering your equipment on time	$\square_5$	$\square_4$	$\square_3$	$\square_2$	$\square_1$	$\square_6$
9. CONDITION OF EQUIPMENT: Equipment was clean and in proper working order	$\square_5$	$\square_4$	$\square_3$	$\square_2$	$\square_1$	$\square_6$
10. INSTRUCTIONS: Showing you safe and proper use of the equipment	$\square_5$	$\square_4$	$\square_3$	$\square_2$	$\square_1$	$\square_6$
11. EMERGENCIES: Showing you what to do in case of an emergency	$\square_5$	$\square_4$	$\square_3$	$\square_2$	$\square_1$	$\square_6$
12. DELIVERY STAFF: How well they did their jobs and how they acted towards you	$\square_5$	$\square_4$	$\square_3$	$\square_2$	$\square_1$	$\square_6$

BILLING

	Excellent	Very Good	Good	Fair	Poor	Doesn't Apply
13. EXPLANATIONS ABOUT COSTS AND HOW TO HANDLE YOUR BILLS: The completeness and accuracy of information and the willingness of staff to answer your questions about the billing	$\square_5$	$\square_4$	$\square_3$	$\square_2$	$\square_1$	$\square_6$
14. APPROPRIATENESS OF CHARGES: The extent to which the bill you received was what you expected to be billed for	$\square_5$	$\square_4$	$\square_3$	$\square_2$	$\square_1$	$\square_6$

LOOKING BACK ON YOUR CARE

	Excellent	Very Good	Good	Fair	Poor	Doesn't Apply
15. HOME HEALTH CARE QUALITY: Overall quality of care and services you received from our company	$\square_5$	$\square_4$	$\square_3$	$\square_2$	$\square_1$	$\square_6$
16. COST AND VALUE OF CARE: Our ability to control patient care costs and provide good value for the money	$\square_5$	$\square_4$	$\square_3$	$\square_2$	$\square_1$	$\square_6$

NCG Research, Inc.

Nashville, Tenn.

Title of Survey: Your Visits to the Doctor's Office: The Patient's Viewpoint

Profile of Organization: NCG Research, Inc. conducts patient satisfaction research for hospitals and physicians.

Date Survey was Created: 1994.

Overview of Survey: N/A

Survey Used to Measure Patient Satisfaction With:

- Quality of medical care received from doctors, health plans, hospitals and other providers (including nurse practitioners, physician assistants and midwives);
- Customer services;
- Costs of care;
- Access to care;
- Coverage;
- Simplicity of educational and other materials;
- Simplicity of paperwork.

Type of Patient Completing Survey: Patients to doctor's offices.

When do Patients/Enrollees Complete Survey?: N/A

Background Information Collected on Those Completing the Survey: N/A

How are Survey Findings Used?: Organizations use the survey for internal process improvement, to satisfy Joint Commission and NCQA requirements, in managed care contract negotiations, to set performance specifications for certain vendor contracts (such as food service), and in facility and strategic market planning.

Date of Last Revision to Survey: Ongoing.

Purchase Price of Survey: Contact NCG Research, Inc. for prices.

Contact Information: Barbara J. McEwen, Sales Manager, NCG Research, Inc., 1321 Murfreesboro Road, Suite 210, P.O. Box 292169, Nashville, Tenn. 37229-2169, (615) 399-0408; fax (615) 399-0608; e-mail bmcewen@ncgresearch.com

Your Visits
to the Doctor's Office:
The Patient's Viewpoint®

Please rate the following things about our office by checking (x) the box below that best answers each question based on your experience. **NOTE:** We are using the term "doctor" throughout this survey to refer to physicians as well as other healthcare professionals, including nurse practitioners, physician assistants, and midwives.

YOUR <u>MOST RECENT VISIT</u> TO OUR OFFICE

	Excellent	Very Good	Good	Fair	Poor	Doesn't Apply
1. Length of time you waited to get an appointment	$\square_5$	$\square_4$	$\square_3$	$\square_2$	$\square_1$	$\square_6$
2. Convenience of the location of the office	$\square_5$	$\square_4$	$\square_3$	$\square_2$	$\square_1$	$\square_6$
3. Getting through to the office by phone	$\square_5$	$\square_4$	$\square_3$	$\square_2$	$\square_1$	$\square_6$
4. Length of time waiting at the office	$\square_5$	$\square_4$	$\square_3$	$\square_2$	$\square_1$	$\square_6$
5. Time spent with the doctor	$\square_5$	$\square_4$	$\square_3$	$\square_2$	$\square_1$	$\square_6$
6. Explanation of what was done for you	$\square_5$	$\square_4$	$\square_3$	$\square_2$	$\square_1$	$\square_6$
7. The technical skills (thoroughness, carefulness, competence) of the doctor you saw	$\square_5$	$\square_4$	$\square_3$	$\square_2$	$\square_1$	$\square_6$
8. The personal manner (courtesy, respect, sensitivity, friendliness) of the doctor you saw	$\square_5$	$\square_4$	$\square_3$	$\square_2$	$\square_1$	$\square_6$
9. This visit overall	$\square_5$	$\square_4$	$\square_3$	$\square_2$	$\square_1$	$\square_6$

10. How many times have you seen this doctor in the past 12 months?

$\square_1$ First visit
$\square_2$ 2 - 3 times
$\square_3$ 4 - 5 times
$\square_4$ 6 - 7 times
$\square_5$ 8 - 9 times
$\square_6$ 10 or more times

11. Was this the doctor you would have preferred to have seen for this care?

$\square_1$ Yes
$\square_0$ No

Q-V900-1/8/96

12. What was the main reason for this visit?
    ☐1 General check-up or examination
    ☐2 Preventive care (such as well-baby visits, school physicals, immunizations or shots)
    ☐3 Care for a sickness or injury (diagnosis, treatment, or follow-up)
    ☐4 Urgent care for a severe condition
    ☐5 Eye examination
    ☐6 Dental care
    ☐7 Emotional or mental health problem (diagnosis, treatment, or follow-up)
    ☐8 Other: (specify)_____

> Please rate the next series of questions based on your **overall** experience with our doctor's office **(NOT just your most recent visit).**

GETTING IN TOUCH WITH THE OFFICE

	Excellent	Very Good	Good	Fair	Poor	Doesn't Apply
13. Getting your telephone calls answered without too many delays or transfers	☐5	☐4	☐3	☐2	☐1	☐6
14. Getting medical information or advice by telephone during regular office hours	☐5	☐4	☐3	☐2	☐1	☐6
15. Getting medical information or advice by telephone during evenings and weekends	☐5	☐4	☐3	☐2	☐1	☐6
16. Courtesy and respect shown to you over the phone	☐5	☐4	☐3	☐2	☐1	☐6
17. How well you have been instructed by the office to deal with a medical emergency situation	☐5	☐4	☐3	☐2	☐1	☐6
18. Length of time you wait between making an appointment for routine care and the day of your visit	☐5	☐4	☐3	☐2	☐1	☐6

ENTERING THE OFFICE

	Excellent	Very Good	Good	Fair	Poor	Doesn't Apply
19. Convenience of this location for you	☐5	☐4	☐3	☐2	☐1	☐6
20. Hours when the doctor's office is open	☐5	☐4	☐3	☐2	☐1	☐6
21. The ease of getting registered, including the amount of time it takes	☐5	☐4	☐3	☐2	☐1	☐6
22. The courtesy and respect shown by the registration staff	☐5	☐4	☐3	☐2	☐1	☐6
23. The forms you must fill out (their number, ease of completing them)	☐5	☐4	☐3	☐2	☐1	☐6
24. How long you wait in the waiting room and exam room before the doctor is able to see you	☐5	☐4	☐3	☐2	☐1	☐6
25. The condition of the waiting area(s)	☐5	☐4	☐3	☐2	☐1	☐6

NCS, Inc.

Edina, Minn.

Title of Software: NCS Viewpoint

Profile of Organization: NCS, Inc. is a global data collection system and services company providing complete solutions for complex mission-critical information processing.

Date Software was Created: November 1994.

Overview of Software: Software uses a combination of custom or standard survey instruments including the SF-36, HSQ and GHAA consumer satisfaction survey to allow user to collect and interpret data that could: (1) target areas for quality improvement; (2) develop medical outcomes; (3) improve administrative efficiencies and enhance marketing efforts, and; (4) meet accreditation criteria in JCAHO, NCQA's HEDIS 2.0 standards.

Software Used to Measure Patient Satisfaction With: Software may be customized to retain information on:

- Quality of medical care received from doctors, health plans and hospitals;
- Customer service;
- Costs of care;
- Access to care;
- Coverage;
- Simplicity of educational and other materials;
- Simplicity of paperwork.

Type of Patient Completing Survey: N/A

When do Patients/Enrollees Complete Survey?: N/A

Background Information Collected on Those Completing the Survey: None.

How are Survey Findings Used?: N/A

Date of Last Revision to Software: N/A

Purchase Price of Software: $995.

Contact Information: Telesales Department, NCS, Inc., 4401 West 76th Street, Minneapolis, Minn. 55435, (800) 347-7226; fax (612) 893-8102.

Cardiac Specialists Group, P.C.

Marking Instructions   0006-01-0001   01
- Use a No.2 Pencil or Black/Blue Ink Pen Only.
- Do Not Use Red Ink or Felt Tip Pens.
- Fill the Oval Completely with a Dark Mark.   ●
- Make No Stray Marks on the Form.
- Fold where Indicated/Return in Envelope Provided.

Curtis David
4442 4th Avenue SE
New York, NY 10022

Rating Scale(s)

SA = Strongly Agree	M = Male	E = Excellent
A = Agree	F = Female	VG = Very Good
N = Neutral		G = Good
D = Disagree		F = Fair
SD = Strongly Disagree		P = Poor

SCHEDULING

1. It was easy getting through to the appointment scheduler.   SA   A   N   D   SD

2. I was able to make an appointment that was convenient to me.   SA   A   N   D   SD

3. It was easy seeing a doctor of my choice.   SA   A   N   D   SD

FACILITY

4. There was adequate parking available.   SA   A   N   D   SD

5. The lobby was comfortable.   SA   A   N   D   SD

ARRIVAL

6. The admission process was efficient.   SA   A   N   D   SD

7. The receptionist was friendly.   SA   A   N   D   SD

8. The receptionist explained my financial responsibilities.   SA   A   N   D   SD

SERVICES

9. How long did you wait in the reception area?   10   15   30   45   >
   (10 = < 10 Minutes, 15 = 10 - 15 Minutes, 30 = 16 - 30 Minutes, 45 = 31 - 45 Minutes,
   > = > 45 Minutes)

10. The amount of time spent in the reception area was acceptable.   SA   A   N   D   SD

11. How long did you wait to be examined by your physician after being seated in the   10   15   30   45   >
    examination room?
    (10 = < 10 Minutes, 15 = 10 - 15 Minutes, 30 = 16 - 30 Minutes, 45 = 31 - 45 Minutes,
    > = > 45 Minutes)

12. The amount of time spent waiting in the examination room was acceptable.   SA   A   N   D   SD

Please turn the page over and complete the survey.

New England HEDIS Coalition
Patient Satisfaction Subcommittee

Boston, Mass.

Title of Survey: NCQA Annual Member Health Care Survey Version 1.0

Profile of Organization: The New England HEDIS Coalition is a group of 18 health plans and 20 employers, consultants and purchasing associations.

Date Survey was Created: 1995.

Overview of Survey: There are 34 questions related to satisfaction with care and services, health status and demographic information. Also, many health plans in the New England HEDIS Coalition have inserted additional questions related to satisfaction with health plan services and mental health and substance abuse services.

Survey Used to Measure Patient Satisfaction With:

■ Quality of medical care received from health plans;

■ Customer services;

■ Costs of care;

■ Access to care;

■ Coverage;

■ Simplicity of paperwork;

■ Availability of information.

Type of Patient Completing Survey: A sample of health plan enrollees.

When do Patients/Enrollees Complete Survey?: March 1996.

Background Information Collected on Those Completing the Survey: Demographic, including date of birth, sex, ethnic background, marital status and level of education.

How are Survey Findings Used?: Reported in the 1995 New England HEDIS Coalition Performance Profile Report.

Date of Last Revision to Survey: N/A

Purchase Price of Survey: N/A

Contact Information: Barbara O. Healy, New England HEDIS Coalition Patient Satisfaction Subcommittee, c/o John Hancock, 200 Berkeley Street, B-12, Boston, Mass. 02117, (617) 572-7087; fax (617) 572-7016.

New Hampshire Hospital Association

Concord, N.H.

Title of Survey: New Hampshire Hospital Association's Patient-Centered Care Project

Profile of Organization: The New Hampshire Hospital Association is a nonprofit affiliate of the American Hospital Association.

Date Survey was Created: December 1995.

Overview of Survey: Survey provides information on patient-related satisfaction and functional status that will improve the delivery of care and integration of services for patients with an acute myocardial infarction or total hip replacement.

Survey Used to Measure Patient Satisfaction With:

- Quality of medical care received from doctors, hospitals and other providers;
- Customer services;
- Access to care;
- Communication between patients and providers;
- Emotional support;
- Home care issues;
- Physician office visit issues;
- Transition and continuity.

Type of Patient Completing Survey: Patients discharged with an acute myocardial infarction or total hip replacement.

When do Patients/Enrollees Complete Survey?: Patients complete the survey at one month, three months and 12 months after discharge from hospital to capture information on the continuum of care.

Background Information Collected on Those Completing the Survey: Demographic.

How are Survey Findings Used?: Findings will be used to provide benchmarks state-wide, allow collaborative quality efforts between providers of care, and to analyze variations in satisfaction and functionality.

Date of Last Revision to Survey: January 1996.

Purchase Price of Survey: Not for sale.

Contact Information: Rachel Rowe, New Hampshire Hospital Association, 125 Airport Road, Concord, N.H. 03301, (603) 225-0900; fax (603) 225-4346; e-mail 74332.164@compuserve.com

North Central Texas HEDIS Coalition

Arlington, Texas

Title of Survey: NCQA Annual Member Health Care Survey, Version 1.0

Profile of Organization: The North Central Texas HEDIS Coalition is a group of health plans, purchasers and consultants working to develop and ensure the use of standardized performance measures for health care.

Date Survey was Created: 1995.

Overview of Survey: Two questions on health plan enrollment; three questions on health services; eight questions on health care and plan; 10 questions on patients' health and daily activities; seven questions "about you"; four questions seeking further information on services.

Survey Used to Measure Patient Satisfaction With:

- Quality of medical care received from doctors and health plans;
- Customer services;
- Costs of care;
- Access to care;
- Coverage;
- Simplicity of paperwork.

Type of Patient Completing Survey: Random sampling.

When do Patients/Enrollees Complete Survey?: Last mailing completed December 1995.

Background Information Collected on Those Completing the Survey: Age; sex; race; marital status; education.

How are Survey Findings Used?: To provide health plan CQI information to purchasers, plan members and potential plan members, and thereby to support more informed decisions about health plan selection.

Date of Last Revision to Survey: 1995.

Purchase Price of Survey: N/A

Contact Information: Shelly Birdsong, Executive Director, North Central Texas HEDIS Coalition, 611 Ryan Plaza Drive, Suite 700, Arlington, Texas 76001, (817) 462-7261; fax (817) 462-6610.

Oxford Health Plans, Inc.

Norwalk, Conn.

Title of Survey: Member Satisfaction With Physician

Profile of Organization: Oxford Health Plans, Inc., is a for-profit IPA-model HMO with over 765,000 members.

Date Survey was Created: 1993.

Overview of Survey: Topics include: overall satisfaction; likelihood to recommend physician to others; office visit wait time; time to schedule appointment; measurement of specific attributes that impact overall satisfaction, such as accessibility and explanation of diagnosis or treatment.

Survey Used to Measure Patient Satisfaction With:

- Quality of medical care received from doctors;
- Access to care;
- Entire office visit process, from initial phone call to follow-up results.

Type of Patient Completing Survey: Patients who have recently visited their primary care provider or OB/GYN.

When do Patients/Enrollees Complete Survey?: Patients are contacted by phone within two to three months of a visit to their primary care provider or OB/GYN.

Background Information Collected on Those Completing the Survey: None.

How are Survey Findings Used?: To report specific results to physicians and aggregate results to QM staff for improvement process.

Date of Last Revision to Survey: September 1995.

Purchase Price of Survey: Not for sale.

Contact Information: Robert Wrinn, Oxford Health Plans, Inc., 800 Connecticut Avenue, Norwalk, Conn. 06854, (203) 851-1782; fax (203) 851-1491.

Pacific Business Group on Health

San Francisco, Calif.

Title of Survey: Health Plan Value Check

Profile of Organization: The Pacific Business Group on Health includes 20 employers providing benefits to over 2.5 million people at a cost of $3 billion annually.

Date Survey was Created: 1989.

Overview of Survey: Questionnaire is divided into eight sections: health plan overall, doctor, other medical care, health plan administration, covered services and costs, other questions about health plan, preventive care and demographics.

Survey Used to Measure Patient Satisfaction With:

- Quality of medical care received from doctors and health plans;
- Customer services;
- Costs of care;
- Access to care;
- Simplicity of paperwork;
- Health improvement programs.

Type of Patient Completing Survey: Employees of participating coalition members.

When do Patients/Enrollees Complete Survey?: Each Spring.

Background Information Collected on Those Completing the Survey: None.

How are Survey Findings Used?: They are used in negotiations with health plans and they are released in summary form to the public.

Date of Last Revision to Survey: September 1995.

Purchase Price of Survey: N/A

Contact Information: David Hopkins, Pacific Business Group on Health, 33 New Montgomery Street, Suite 1450, San Francisco, Calif. 94105, (415) 281-8660; fax (415) 281-0960.

Parkside Associates, Inc.

Park Ridge, Ill.

Title of Survey: Long-Term Care Quality of Care Monitor®

Profile of Organization: Parkside Associates, Inc., affiliated with Advocate Health Care, provides quality survey systems and reporting mechanisms for the health care industry.

Date Survey was Created: 1995.

Overview of Survey: Survey consists of 54 questions developed and tested for reliability and validity through focus groups, pilot testing and national testing with over 150 facilities. Response categories include a combination of evaluative ratings ("excellent" to "poor"), yes/no, and frequency of occurrence ("always" to "never").

Survey Used to Measure Patient Satisfaction With:

- Quality of medical care received at nursing homes;
- Comfort and cleanliness;
- Nursing care;
- Facility care and services;
- Food service;
- Reasons for facility choice;
- Restorative care.

Type of Patient Completing Survey: Long-term care residents or their responsible parties.

When do Patients/Enrollees Complete Survey?: Annually or semiannually.

Background Information Collected on Those Completing the Survey: Demographics.

How are Survey Findings Used?: Quality improvement; marketing and public relations; accreditation; goal setting.

Date of Last Revision to Survey: December 1995.

Purchase Price of Survey: Contact Parkside Associates for pricing information.

Contact Information: Tina K. Cooper, Parkside Associates, Inc., 205 West Touhy Avenue, Suite 204, Park Ridge, Ill. 60068-4282, (847) 698-9866; fax (847) 698-6875.

QUALITY OF CARE MONITOR
SATISFACTION SURVEY

Directions:
Below are a number of questions about our resident care and services. Please answer each question by circling the number that best indicates your opinion. If the resident is able to assist in the completion of the survey, feel free to include his/her feedback.

If the resident has been at our facility for an extended length of time, please answer only about how **you currently feel.** Also, if a question does not apply to your situation, circle "Don't Know" or "Does Not Apply." Your answers will help us to improve our services.

☐ Please check here if the resident completed or helped complete the survey.   (1)

OVERALL RATINGS

What is your overall opinion of:	Poor	Fair	Good	Very Good	Excellent	Does Not Apply
1. The quality of care received?	5	4	3	2	1	NA
2. Nursing care?	5	4	3	2	1	NA
3. Physician care?	5	4	3	2	1	NA
4. Social workers?	5	4	3	2	1	NA
5. Housekeeping services?	5	4	3	2	1	NA
6. Food service?	5	4	3	2	1	NA
7. Administration?	5	4	3	2	1	NA
8. Mail service?	5	4	3	2	1	NA
9. Billing?	5	4	3	2	1	NA (10)

FACILITY CARE & SERVICES

	No	To Some Extent	Yes	Don't Know
1. Does the staff adequately explain the resident's condition and care plan?	3	2	1	DK
2. Does the facility offer an adequate range of activities and recreation?	3	2	1	DK
3. Is the resident given all of the care and services he/she needs?	3	2	1	DK
4. Does the facility encourage appropriate family members' or friends' involvement with the resident's care?	3	2	1	DK
5. Are your (the resident's) preferences and choices respected by the staff?	3	2	1	DK
6. When a physician is needed, can one be seen promptly?	3	2	1	DK
7. Would you recommend this facility to your family and friends?	3	2	1	DK (17)

COMFORT AND CLEANLINESS

How would you rate the:	Poor	Fair	Good	Very Good	Excellent
1. Cleanliness of the resident's room?	5	4	3	2	1
2. Temperature and ventilation of the resident's room?	5	4	3	2	1
3. Protection of personal property?	5	4	3	2	1
4. Comfort of the resident's room?	5	4	3	2	1
5. Cleanliness of the facility in general?	5	4	3	2	1
6. Ability to personalize the resident's room?	5	4	3	2	1
7. Scent within the facility?	5	4	3	2	1 (24)

NURSING CARE

	Never	Rarely	Sometimes	Often	Always	Don't Know
1. Do the nurses call you (the resident) by name?	5	4	3	2	1	DK
2. Do you (the resident) feel comfortable about sharing personal concerns with the nursing staff?	5	4	3	2	1	DK
3. Do you feel the nursing staff treats you (the resident) with respect and dignity?	5	4	3	2	1	DK
4. Do you (the resident) receive satisfactory answers to questions from the nursing staff?	5	4	3	2	1	DK
5. Does the nursing staff seem to know what they are doing?	5	4	3	2	1	DK
6. When there is a concern or problem, do you (the resident) know who to go to for help?	5	4	3	2	1	DK
7. Are medications given in a timely manner?	5	4	3	2	1	DK
8. Does it appear there is an adequate number of staff available?	5	4	3	2	1	DK
9. Is adequate attention given to personal grooming needs?	5	4	3	2	1	DK (33)

Parkside Associates, Inc.

Park Ridge, Ill.

Title of Survey: Home Healthcare Quality of Care Monitor®

Profile of Organization: Parkside Associates, Inc., affiliated with Advocate Health Care, provides quality survey systems and reporting mechanisms for the health care industry.

Date Survey was Created: 1995.

Overview of Survey: Survey consists of 56 questions developed and tested for reliability and validity through focus groups, pilot testing and national testing with over 180 agencies. Response categories include a combination of evaluative ratings ("excellent" to "poor"), yes/no, and frequency of occurrence ("always" to "never").

Survey Used to Measure Patient Satisfaction With:

- Quality of medical care received from home care providers;
- Customer services;
- Access to care;
- Care process;
- Patient involvement and education;
- Orientation to home care;
- Perceived medical outcome;
- Professional manner of staff;
- Reasons for choosing agency.

Type of Patient Completing Survey: Random sample of current or discharged patients receiving home health services.

When do Patients/Enrollees Complete Survey?: Post-discharge.

Background Information Collected on Those Completing the Survey: Demographics.

How are Survey Findings Used?: Quality improvement; marketing and public relations; accreditation; goal setting.

Date of Last Revision to Survey: January 1996.

Purchase Price of Survey: Contact Parkside Associates for pricing information.

Contact Information: Tina K. Cooper, Parkside Associates, Inc., 205 West Touhy Avenue, Suite 204, Park Ridge, Ill. 60068-4282, (847) 698-9866; fax (847) 698-6875.

HOME HEALTHCARE
QUALITY OF CARE MONITOR

Directions: Below are a number of questions about your recent home care. Please answer each question by circling the number that best indicates your opinion about the service you received. If a question does not apply to your situation, circle "Does Not Apply." If the patient cannot complete the survey, a family member is encouraged to do so for him or her.

☐ Please check here if a family member completed the survey.

OVERALL RATINGS	Poor	Fair	Good	Very Good	Excellent	Does Not Apply
Please rate:						
1. The overall quality of home care service?	5	4	3	2	1	☐
2. If you had more than one visit, please rate the coordination of your home care services over time?	5	4	3	2	1	☐
3. The professional manner of the staff?	5	4	3	2	1	☐
4. The convenience of scheduled visits?	5	4	3	2	1	☐
5. The nurses overall?	5	4	3	2	1	☐
6. The home health aides overall?	5	4	3	2	1	☐

BEGINNING YOUR HOME CARE	No	To Some Extent	Yes	Does Not Apply
1. Did the home care staff clearly explain what to expect during your home care?	3	2	1	☐
2. Were you told what to do if you needed immediate medical attention from the agency?	3	2	1	☐
3. Were you told how to voice a complaint?	3	2	1	☐
4. Did home care services start as soon as you expected?	3	2	1	☐
5. Did the home care staff clearly and completely explain your rights and responsibilities?	3	2	1	☐
6. Did the staff explain who to call for questions or additional services?	3	2	1	☐
7. Did the staff discuss home safety with you?	3	2	1	☐
8. Did the staff discuss a diet plan with you?	3	2	1	☐

Parkside Associates, Inc.

Park Ridge, Ill.

Title of Surveys: Quality of Care Monitor® Patient Surveys

Profile of Organization: Parkside Associates, Inc., affiliated with Advocate Health Care, provides quality survey systems and reporting mechanisms for the health care industry.

Date Surveys were Created: 1990.

Overview of Survey: Surveys consists of 30-55 questions developed and tested for reliability and validity through focus groups, pilot testing and national testing with over 600 facilities. Response categories include a combination of evaluative ratings ("excellent" to "poor") and yes/no.

Surveys Used to Measure Patient Satisfaction With:

- Quality of medical care received from doctors, hospitals, emergency rooms and other providers;

- Customer services;

- Access to care;

- Others, including: nursing care; physician care; medical outcomes; food service; comfort and cleanliness; delivery of care; admitting/registration; billing; staff courtesy; willingness to return to and recommend facility; testing services; waiting time; side-effects.

Type of Patient Completing Surveys: Random sample of recent discharges.

When do Patients/Enrollees Complete Surveys?: Post-discharge.

Background Information Collected on Those Completing the Surveys: Demographics.

How are Survey Findings Used?: Quality improvement; marketing and public relations; accreditation; goal setting.

Date of Last Revisions to Surveys: Inpatient, 1993; Emergency room, 1994; Outpatient surgery, 1996; Outpatient testing and therapy, 1996; Inpatient psychiatric, 1996/7.

Purchase Price of Surveys: Contact Parkside Associates for pricing information.

Contact Information: Tina K. Cooper, Parkside Associates, Inc., 205 West Touhy Avenue, Suite 204, Park Ridge, Ill. 60068-4282, (847) 698-9866; fax (847) 698-6875.

Outpatient
Quality of Care Monitor

Directions:

Below are a number of questions about your **recent outpatient visit**. Please answer each question by checking the box that best indicates your opinion about the treatment you received. If the patient is a minor/child or cannot complete the survey, a family member is encouraged to do so for him or her.

If you received therapy or were tested in more than one area, answer all questions based on your experience with the treatment indicated below. If a question does not apply to your situation, check "Does Not Apply". Your answers will help us to improve our services.

☐ Please check here if someone other than the patient is completing the survey. (105)

TREATMENT AREAS

[01] Lab/Pathology	[03] GI Lab	[21] Physical Therapy
[02] X-Ray (Radiology)	[06] Eye Service	[22] Occupational Therapy
[04] Nuclear Medicine	[07] Blood Donor Program	[23] Speech Therapy
[05] MRI	[08] Heart Testing	[24] Cardiac Rehab
[09] CT Scan	[11] EKG	[25] Radiation Therapy
[10] Ultrasound	[12] EEG	[26] Respiratory Therapy
		[27] Chemotherapy (21-22)

BEFORE YOUR TEST OR THERAPY	Yes	To Some Extent	No	Does Not Apply	
1. a.) Was your visit pre-scheduled?	[1]		[3]	[4]	(23)
b.) If pre-scheduled, was your visit at a convenient time?	[1]	[2]	[3]	[4]	
2. Were the pre-visit medical instructions clear and understandable?	[1]	[2]	[3]	[4]	
3. Was the registration process handled without any problems?	[1]	[2]	[3]	[4]	
4. Did you receive satisfactory answers to your questions from registration personnel?	[1]	[2]	[3]	[4]	
5. Was the waiting time acceptable a.) in the registration area?	[1]	[2]	[3]	[4]	
b.) in the treatment area?	[1]	[2]	[3]	[4]	(29)

How would you rate the:	Excellent	Good	Fair	Poor	Very Poor	Does Not Apply	
6. Ease in obtaining an appointment?	[1]	[2]	[3]	[4]	[5]	[6]	
7. Comfort of the waiting area?	[1]	[2]	[3]	[4]	[5]	[6]	
8. Signs within the facility?	[1]	[2]	[3]	[4]	[5]	[6]	
9. Parking?	[1]	[2]	[3]	[4]	[5]	[6]	(33)

Outpatient Surgery
Quality of Care Monitor

Directions:

Below are a number of questions about your **recent outpatient surgery** visit. Please answer each question by checking the box that best indicates your opinion. If the patient is a minor/child or cannot complete the survey, a family member may do so for him or her.

If you (the patient) have been a patient at our facility before, please answer only about your **last visit**. Also, if a question does not apply to your situation, check "Does Not Apply." Your answers will help us to improve our services.

☐ Please check here if someone other than the patient is completing the survey. (1)

FIRST IMPRESSIONS	Yes	To Some Extent	No	Does Not Apply	
1. Did the admitting or registration person take time to answer your questions?	1	2	3	4	(2)
2. If your visit was pre-scheduled, was it scheduled at a time convenient for you?	1	2	3	4	
3. Was the waiting time acceptable:					
a. To be registered?	1	2	3	4	
b. To see a nurse?	1	2	3	4	
c. To see a physician?	1	2	3	4	
d. To receive treatment?	1	2	3	4	
4. Were you seen by your own physician at our facility?	1		3	4	
5. Did you feel that the nurses were concerned about you as a person?	1	2	3	4	
6. Did you receive satisfactory answers to your questions from the nurses who treated you?	1	2	3	4	
7. Did the nurses who treated you seem to know what they were doing?	1	2	3	4	
8. Did you stay at the hospital overnight?	1		3		(12)

(Copyright 1994, Parkside Associates, Inc.)

QUALITY OF CARE MONITOR

Directions:
Below are a number of questions about your **recent hospital stay**. Please answer each question by checking the box that best indicates your opinion. If the patient is a minor/child or cannot complete the survey, family members may do so for him or her.

If you (the patient) have been a patient at this hospital before, please answer only about your **most recent stay**. Also, if a question doesn't apply to your situation, check "Does Not Apply." Your answers will help us to improve our services.

☐ Please check here if someone other than the patient is completing the survey. (167)

RETURNING HOME	Yes	To Some Extent	No	Does Not Apply	
1. Do you feel the **condition** for which you were admitted to the hospital has **improved** as much as expected?	☐1	☐2	☐3	☐4	(21)
2. Were you satisfied with how well your **pain** was **controlled**?	☐1	☐2	☐3	☐4	(22)
3. Were you satisfied with the **thoroughness of care** you received from your **physicians**?	☐1	☐2	☐3	☐4	(23)
4. Did your **physicians** adequately **explain** your diagnosis and treatment to you?	☐1	☐2	☐3	☐4	(24)
5. Were you sent **home** from the hospital **before** you felt **ready**?	☐1	☐2	☐3	☐4	(25)
6. Were your **religious (spiritual) needs** adequately met?	☐1	☐2	☐3	☐4	(26)
7. When you left the hospital, did you have a **better understanding** of your illness than when you entered?	☐1	☐2	☐3	☐4	(27)
8. Before you were discharged, did the hospital staff **prepare you** or your caregiver to manage your care at home?	☐1	☐2	☐3	☐4	(28)
9. Would you **return** to this hospital for your medical care?	☐1	☐2	☐3	☐4	(29)
10. Would you **recommend** this hospital to your friends or family?	☐1	☐2	☐3	☐4	(30)
11. Overall, are you satisfied with the outcome of your medical treatment?	☐1	☐2	☐3	☐4	(31)

(32-33) (Blnk)

COURTESY	Excellent	Good	Fair	Poor	Very Poor	Does Not Apply	
How would you rate the **courtesy** of the following people:							
1. Admitting personnel?	☐1	☐2	☐3	☐4	☐5	☐6	(34)
2. Nurses?	☐1	☐2	☐3	☐4	☐5	☐6	
3. Physicians?	☐1	☐2	☐3	☐4	☐5	☐6	
4. People who drew blood?	☐1	☐2	☐3	☐4	☐5	☐6	(37)
5. Housekeeping staff?	☐1	☐2	☐3	☐4	☐5	☐6	
6. People delivering your food?	☐1	☐2	☐3	☐4	☐5	☐6	
7. Escort people?	☐1	☐2	☐3	☐4	☐5	☐6	(40)
8. Switchboard personnel?	☐1	☐2	☐3	☐4	☐5	☐6	
9. Physical therapists?	☐1	☐2	☐3	☐4	☐5	☐6	
10. People who provided breathing therapy?	☐1	☐2	☐3	☐4	☐5	☐6	(43)
11. X-ray/Radiology personnel?	☐1	☐2	☐3	☐4	☐5	☐6	
12. Chaplains?	☐1	☐2	☐3	☐4	☐5	☐6	
13. Social workers?	☐1	☐2	☐3	☐4	☐5	☐6	(46)
14. Volunteers?	☐1	☐2	☐3	☐4	☐5	☐6	
15. Cashiers?	☐1	☐2	☐3	☐4	☐5	☐6	

(49-51) (Blnk)

QUALITY OF
CARE MONITOR®

Directions:

Below are a number of questions about your **recent emergency department** visit.
Please answer each question by circling the number that best indicates your opinion.
If the patient is a minor (child) or cannot complete the survey, a family member may do so for him or her.

If you (the patient) have been a patient in our emergency department before, please answer only about your **last visit**. Also, if a question does not apply to your situation, circle "Does Not Apply". Your answers will help us to improve our services.

☐ Please check here if someone other than the patient is completing the survey. (1)

FIRST IMPRESSIONS

	YES	TO SOME EXTENT	NO	DOES NOT APPLY
1. Did the admitting or registration person take time to answer your questions?	1	2	3	4 (2)
2. Was the waiting time acceptable:				
a. To be registered?	1	2	3	4
b. To see a nurse?	1	2	3	4
c. To see a physician?	1	2	3	4
d. To receive treatment?	1	2	3	4
3. Were you seen by your own physician in our emergency department?	1		3	4
4. Did you feel the nurses were concerned about you as a person?	1	2	3	4
5. Did you receive satisfactory answers to your questions from the physicians who treated you?	1	2	3	4
6. Did the physicians who treated you seem to know what they were doing?	1	2	3	4
7. Did you stay at the hospital overnight?	1		3	

Parkside Associates, Inc.

Park Ridge, Ill.

Title of Survey: Physician Office/Clinic Quality of Care Monitor®

Profile of Organization: Parkside Associates, Inc., affiliated with Advocate Health Care, provides quality survey systems and reporting mechanisms for the health care industry.

Date Survey was Created: 1993.

Overview of Survey: Survey consists of 54 questions developed and tested for reliability and validity through focus groups, pilot testing and national testing with over 170 practices. Response categories are designed as evaluative ratings ("excellent" to "poor").

Survey Used to Measure Patient Satisfaction With:

- Quality of medical care received during physician office/clinic visit.
- Customer services;
- Access to care;
- Others, including: physician care; nursing care; front office services; testing services; billing; facility characteristics; reasons for physician/clinic choice.

Type of Patient Completing Survey: Random sample of recent visits.

When do Patients/Enrollees Complete Survey?: Post-physician office/clinic visit.

Background Information Collected on Those Completing the Survey: Demographics.

How are Survey Findings Used?: Quality improvement; marketing and public relations; managed care (as "report cards").

Date of Last Revision to Survey: N/A

Purchase Price of Survey: Contact Parkside Associates for pricing information.

Contact Information: Tina K. Cooper, Parkside Associates, Inc., 205 West Touhy Avenue, Suite 204, Park Ridge, Ill. 60068-4282, (847) 698-9866; fax (847) 698-6875.

PHYSICIAN OFFICE
QUALITY OF CARE MONITOR

Directions:

Below are a number of questions about your **recent physician office visit**. Please answer each question by checking the box that best indicates your opinion about the service you received. If a question does not apply to your situation, check "Does Not Apply". If the patient is a minor/child or cannot complete the survey, a family member is encouraged to do so for him or her.

1️⃣ Please check here if someone other than the patient is completing the survey.   (150)

Before Your Office Visit

How would you rate the:

	Excellent	Very Good	Good	Fair	Poor	Does Not Apply	
1. Ease in getting through to the doctor's office by phone.	1	2	3	4	5	6	(1)
2. Courtesy of staff taking your call.	1	2	3	4	5	6	
3. Availability of the **doctor** to talk on the phone during office hours.	1	2	3	4	5	6	
4. Availability of a **nurse** to talk on the phone during office hours.	1	2	3	4	5	6	
5. Time between making an appointment and the day of your visit.	1	2	3	4	5	6	
6. Convenience of office hours.	1	2	3	4	5	6	
7. Ease in seeing the doctor of your choice.	1	2	3	4	5	6	
8. Convenience of the location of the doctor's office.	1	2	3	4	5	6	
9. Parking convenience.	1	2	3	4	5	6	(9)

(10-12) (Blnk)

At the Time of Your Visit

How would you rate:

	Excellent	Very Good	Good	Fair	Poor	Does Not Apply	
1. The courtesy of the office receptionist.	1	2	3	4	5	6	(13)
2. The registration process (simplicity, speed, etc.).	1	2	3	4	5	6	
3. The comfort of the waiting area.	1	2	3	4	5	6	
4. The waiting time to see the doctor.	1	2	3	4	5	6	(16)

• How long did you wait? 1️⃣ 1 - 5 min.   4️⃣ 31 - 45 min.
2️⃣ 6 - 15 min.   5️⃣ 46 - 1 hour
3️⃣ 16 - 30 min.   6️⃣ over 1 hour

	Excellent	Very Good	Good	Fair	Poor	Does Not Apply	
5. The **overall quality of care** you received.	1	2	3	4	5	6	(18)
6. The doctor overall.	1	2	3	4	5	6	
7. The nurse overall.	1	2	3	4	5	6	
8. The amount of time spent with the doctor.	1	2	3	4	5	6	
9. The doctor's explanation of what was done for you (tests, diagnosis, treatment).	1	2	3	4	5	6	
10. The thoroughness of care you received from the doctor.	1	2	3	4	5	6	
11. How well the nurse answered your questions.	1	2	3	4	5	6	(24)

Parkside Associates, Inc.

Park Ridge, Ill.

Title of Survey: NCQA Annual Member Health Care Survey (See **National Commission on Quality Assurance** entry on Page 52.)

Profile of Organization: Parkside Associates, Inc., affiliated with Advocate Health Care, provides quality survey systems and reporting mechanisms for the health care industry.

Date Survey was Created: 1995.

Overview of Survey: Survey was designed by NCQA to meet their accreditation recommendations. It is based on their HEDIS 3.0 survey and includes the SF-12.

Survey Used to Measure Patient Satisfaction With:

- Quality of medical care received from doctors, health plans, hospitals and other providers;
- Customer services;
- Costs of care;
- Access to care;
- Coverage;
- Functional status (SF-12).

Type of Patient Completing Survey: Random sample of plan members.

When do Patients/Enrollees Complete Survey?: Once annually.

Background Information Collected on Those Completing the Survey: None.

How are Survey Findings Used?: Accreditation and marketing in managed care.

Date of Last Revision to Survey: 1995.

Purchase Price of Survey: Contact Parkside Associates.

Contact Information: Tina K. Cooper, Parkside Associates, Inc., 205 West Touhy Avenue, Suite 204, Park Ridge, Ill. 60068-4282, (847) 698-9866; fax (847) 698-6875.

Press, Ganey Associates
South Bend, Ind.

Title of Survey: Press, Ganey Satisfaction Measurement Surveys

Profile of Organization: Press, Ganey Associates specializes in developing patient satisfaction survey instruments and consulting to clients on quality improvement programs.

Date Survey was Created: N/A

Overview of Survey: Press, Ganey has developed a full range of satisfaction measurement services for the health care industry. The surveys cover the full range of experiences within the continuum of care. Standard survey questions include aspects of customer service, interpersonal interactions, amenities and physical plant. Surveys can also include customized questions. Comprehensive management reports permit internal and external benchmarking. External benchmarking is achieved by comparisons to Press, Ganey's national databases.

Survey Used to Measure Patient Satisfaction With: Press, Ganey creates satisfaction measurement surveys in the following areas:

- Inpatient hospital services;
- Emergency room/outpatient/ambulatory services;
- Physician office visit services;
- Managed care health plans;
- Home health care services and long-term care providers;
- Outcomes measurement.

Type of Patient Completing Survey: See above.

When do Patients/Enrollees Complete Survey?: Surveys are generally mailed to patients three to five days post-discharge (or post-encounter for ambulatory areas).

Background Information Collected on Those Completing the Survey: Demographic.

How are Survey Findings Used?: Surveys allow clients to identify areas needing improvements; monitor the impact of QI programs on patient satisfaction; evaluate quality improvement with specific experiences by unit, service specialty, shift and department through the eyes of patients; generate planning information to focus resources for attracting and keeping patients; and compare satisfaction scores with external standards based on current performance of hundreds of health care organizations in national databases.

Date of Last Revision to Survey: Ongoing.

Purchase Price of Survey: All surveys are priced between $300-$4,500, depending on the service and number of reports.

Contact Information: John Gordon, Press, Ganey Associates, Corporate/Central Offices, 1657 Commerce Drive, South Bend, Ind. 46628, (219) 232-3387; fax (219) 232-3485.

Prudential HealthCare Plan of California, Inc.

Woodland Hills, Calif.

Title of Survey: N/A

Profile of Organization: Prudential HealthCare HMO is offered by Prudential HealthCare Plan of California, Inc., a subsidiary of the Prudential Insurance Company of America.

Date Survey was Created: N/A

Overview of Survey: Survey consists of 25 to 50 questions.

Survey Used to Measure Patient Satisfaction With:
- Quality of medical care received from doctors, health plans and other providers;
- Customer services;
- Costs of care;
- Access to care;
- Coverage;
- Simplicity of educational and other materials;
- Simplicity of paperwork.

Type of Patient Completing Survey: All subscribers are given the option to participate in survey.

When do Patients/Enrollees Complete Survey?: Annually.

Background Information Collected on Those Completing the Survey: None.

How are Survey Findings Used?: To improve customer satisfaction and identify possible areas of abuse. Also to assist on final financial reimbursement to medical groups.

Date of Last Revision to Survey: 1995.

Purchase Price of Survey: Not for sale.

Contact Information: Leta M. Lager, Prudential HealthCare Plan of California, 5800 Canoga Avenue, Woodland Hills, Calif. 91367, (818) 888-5861; fax (818) 392-2288.
433-3150

Quality Management Consultants, Inc.
Des Moines, Iowa

Title of Survey: Patient Satisfaction Survey

Profile of Organization: Quality Management Consultants, Inc. provides health care quality improvement consulting for doctors, clinics, hospitals and other health care providers. The firm also provides health care cost reduction analysis and consulting for business and industry.

Date Survey was Created: N/A

Overview of Survey: A one-page survey with 15 "yes or no" and "rate your satisfaction level" questions, with space for additional comments.

Survey Used to Measure Patient Satisfaction With:

- Quality of medical care received from doctors, health plans and other providers;
- Customer services;
- Costs of care;
- Access to care;
- Convenience;
- Coverage;
- Simplicity of educational and other materials.

Type of Patient Completing Survey: A random sample of physician office, geriatric care, ambulatory care, optometry, chiropractic and home health care patients.

When do Patients/Enrollees Complete Survey?: Following an appointment or visit.

Background Information Collected on Those Completing the Survey: Why the patient chose this provider; reason for visit to the provider (check-up or specific problem).

How are Survey Findings Used?: To initiate CQI projects.

Date of Last Revision to Survey: December 1995.

Purchase Price of Survey: $200 each.

Contact Information: Mary Krieg, Quality Management Consultants, Inc., 691 Harwood Drive, Des Moines, Iowa 50312, (515) 255-2576; fax (515) 255-4036; e-mail mmkrieg@aol.com

Quantum Health Resources

Indianapolis, Ind.

Title of Survey: Quantum Health Resources Customer Satisfaction Survey

Profile of Organization: Quantum Health Resources is a home health care-based company servicing patients with rare and severe chronic disorders.

Date Survey was Created: 1993.

Overview of Survey: Survey consists of 25 questions/statements divided into two parts, with response categories including "strongly agree," "somewhat agree," "somewhat disagree," and "strongly disagree."

Survey Used to Measure Patient Satisfaction With:

- Quality of medical care received from Quantum clinicians and support personnel;

- Access to care;

- Whether patients are treated with respect and dignity by provider's caregivers;

- Whether a care program provides adequate access to treatment or service;

- Whether patient's clinical concerns about their treatment are being addressed;

- Whether patients are involved with and empowered to participate in their own care.

Type of Patient Completing Survey: Home health patients.

When do Patients/Enrollees Complete Survey?: In 1994, Quantum surveyed all patients. In 1995, the survey was mailed to all new patients.

Background Information Collected on Those Completing the Survey: None.

How are Survey Findings Used?: Internally, the results are used to guide Quantum's quality improvement program. Externally, by Quantum's operations, sales and marketing divisions.

Date of Last Revision to Survey: Revision in progress.

Purchase Price of Survey: N/A

Contact Information: Barbara Pantos, Quantum Health Resources, Two Parkwood Crossing, 310 East 96th Street, Suite 300, Indianapolis, Ind. 46240, (317) 580-6830; fax (317) 580-6842.

Sachs Group
Evanston, Ill.

Title of Survey: Sachs/Scarborough HealthPlus

Profile of Organization: The Sachs Group performs market research for, and consults to, the health care industry.

Date Survey was Created: 1994.

Overview of Survey: Questions are asked about the following topics: health status; satisfaction with health plan/health insurance coverage; attitudes about health care/psychographics; utilization of hospital services; physician usage; demographics.

Survey Used to Measure Patient Satisfaction With:

- Quality of medical care received from doctors, health plans and hospitals;
- Customer services;
- Costs of care;
- Access to care;
- Coverage;
- Simplicity of paperwork.

Type of Patient Completing Survey: Consumers in 27 markets are surveyed via random digit dialing and a written questionnaire.

When do Patients/Enrollees Complete Survey?: N/A

Background Information Collected on Those Completing the Survey: Demographics and consumer habits/preferences regarding television, radio station, newspaper and magazine readership, retail, shopping preferences, etc.

How are Survey Findings Used?: Business planning, decision-making, media planning, consumer satisfaction measurement, competitor analysis.

Date of Last Revision to Survey: 1995.

Purchase Price of Survey: Depends on package ordered.

Contact Information: Jenny Rode, manager of communications, Sachs Group, 1800 Sherman Avenue, Suite 609, Evanston, Ill. 60201, (847) 475-7526; fax (847) 475-7830; e-mail jrode@sachs.com

SmartTalk, Inc.

Salt Lake City, Utah

Title of Survey: SmartSurvey Automated Survey System

Profile of Organization: SmartTalk, Inc. produces patient communications tools for the health care industry.

Date Survey was Created: N/A

Overview of Survey: Requests a touch-tone or spoken (optional) response to questions providers design. Patients are surveyed automatically by phone. Survey data can be exported for analysis.

Survey Used to Measure Patient Satisfaction With:

- Quality of medical care received from doctors, health plans, hospitals and other providers;
- Customer services;
- Costs of care;
- Access to care;
- Coverage;
- Simplicity of educational and other materials;
- Simplicity of paperwork.

Type of Patient Completing Survey: Those that can be reached by phone.

When do Patients/Enrollees Complete Survey?: When they are called by the system. Attempts to contact the patient continue over a designated time period.

Background Information Collected on Those Completing the Survey: Any information that can be phrased to elicit a touch-tone or verbal yes/no/numeric response.

How are Survey Findings Used?: SmartSurvey tabulates results and prints reports of every response. Response data can also be exported to spreadsheet or statistics software for further analysis.

Date of Last Revision to Survey: N/A

Purchase Price of Survey: Call for quote.

Contact Information: Paul Guertin, sales representative, SmartTalk, Inc., 1100 East 6600 South, Suite 320, Salt Lake City, Utah 84121, (800) 888-7274; fax (801) 265-8880.

Tennessee Managed Care Organization

Nashville, Tenn.

Title of Survey: Tenncare Member Satisfaction Survey

Profile of Organization: Tennessee Managed Care Organization is a network model health plan serving over 335,000 enrollees in the state. The plan has 51 clinics, contracts with and/or uses 102 hospitals, and has over 2,500 physicians in the network.

Date Survey was Created: October 1994.

Overview of Survey: Eleven questions designed to glean information from members on their perception of managed care and the operation of the Tennessee Managed Care Network.

Survey Used to Measure Patient Satisfaction With:

- Quality of medical care received from health plan;
- Customer services;
- Access to care.

Type of Patient Completing Survey: Health plan members.

When do Patients/Enrollees Complete Survey?: Twice annually.

Background Information Collected on Those Completing the Survey: Demographic.

How are Survey Findings Used?: To address development issues.

Date of Last Revision to Survey: May 1996.

Purchase Price of Survey: Not for sale.

Contact Information: Colleen Smeekens, Tennessee Managed Care Organization, 210 Athens Way, Nashville, Tenn. 37228, (615) 329-2016; fax (615) 329-0250.

UltraLink, Inc.

Costa Mesa, Calif.

Title of Survey: UltraLink National Survey of Member Satisfaction with Managed Care Plans

Profile of Organization: UltraLink is a network manager that assists national companies in implementing flexible, cost-effective and high quality health care plans for geographically dispersed employees, both active and retired. UltraLink's team of health care professionals works closely with health benefits staff to select, implement and manage the most appropriate health care delivery system for each location.

Date Survey was Created: 1995.

Overview of Survey: The survey consists of 16 questions and is administered by professional surveyors by telephone. The questions can be categorized by: overall health, access, outcomes of treatment, prescription services, communications and service, worth & value of health care coverage to the member.

Survey Used to Measure Patient Satisfaction With:

■ Quality of medical care received from doctors and health plans;

■ Customer services;

■ Costs of care;

■ Access to care;

■ Coverage.

Type of Patient Completing Survey: Random sample of subscribers.

When do Patients/Enrollees Complete Survey?: Annually in the spring by telephone.

Background Information Collected on Those Completing the Survey: Age; sex; number of years with health plan; health status.

How are Survey Findings Used: Data is compiled, analyzed, benchmarked and formally reported to UltraLink clients with narratives, tables and graphs. Data is shared with health plans. Health plans with values falling below the benchmarks are contacted and action plans for improvement are developed. Survey findings are used by national employers to help define their network of health plans, identify needs for improved health service and determine the value of the health benefit they are offering to their employees.

Date of Last Revision to Survey: February 1996. UltraLink will be completing the 1996 national survey in May.

Purchase Price of Survey: A report of UltraLink's *aggregated* national survey with analysis may be purchased for $500.

Contact Information: Vicki Sharp, UltraLink, Inc., 3515 Harbor Boulevard, Costa Mesa, Calif. 92626, (714) 513-6356; fax (714) 513-6399; e-mail 103454.1676@compuserve.com

The Survey Instrument

The following questions were included in this year's survey. The first ten questions were rated on a scale of <u>excellent, very good, good, fair, poor:</u>

1. Overall, how would you evaluate the healthcare at your current plan?

2. How would you rate the convenience of location and hours of the doctor's office?

3. How would you rate access to your Primary Care Physician?

4. How would you rate access to specialty care if you need it?

5. How would you rate the services available for getting prescriptions filled?

6. How would you rate the explanations of medical procedures and tests?

7. How would you rate the advice you get about ways to avoid illness and stay healthy?

8. How would you rate the thoroughness of treatment you receive?

9. How would you rate the care you receive from your Primary Care Physician?

10. How would you rate the overall customer service you receive from your HMO?

11. Would you recommend your current health plan to your family and friends?

Definitely Yes	Probably Not
Probably Yes	Definitely Not

12. Considering the amount of money that you and your employer pay for your health care, how would you rate the <u>worth or value</u> that you receive from your HMO?

> Excellent - Very Good - Good - Fair - Poor

13. Do you have any comments about your health plans?

14. Would you say your health is excellent, very good, good, fair, or poor?

15. How long have you been enrolled in your HMO?

16. How old were you on your last birthday?

Responses were aggregated into six categories for this summary report. The data was categorized as follows:

Category	Questions
Overall Health	1, 14
Access	2,3,4
Outcomes	1,8,9
Prescription Services	5
Communications, Service	6,7,10,12
Recommend this HMO	11
Customer Service	10
Worth and Value	12

Appendix

HHS Office of Inspector General Report:
HMO Customer Satisfaction Surveys

The following information is excerpted from a report of the Office of Inspector General (OIG) at the U.S. Department of Health and Human Services. To obtain a complete copy of the report (OEI-O2-00360, March 1995), contact the OIG's New York Regional Office at (212) 264-1998.

E X E C U T I V E   S U M M A R Y

PURPOSE

To assess how Medicare health maintenance organizations (HMOs) are conducting customer satisfaction surveys and how they are utilizing the results of these surveys.

BACKGROUND

In various staff meetings, the Office of Managed Care in the Health Care Financing Administration (HCFA) asked the Office of Inspector General (OIG) to survey how Medicare HMOs are measuring customer satisfaction, particularly of Medicare beneficiaries, and using the resulting data. The HCFA requested this study in order to better ascertain how active its role should be in surveying Medicare HMO enrollees and how the surveys HMOs are conducting can be of use to HCFA in its monitoring efforts.

We selected a stratified random sample of 95 HMO risk and cost contracts out of the universe of 185 such contracts with Medicare beneficiaries enrolled as of February 1, 1995. We sent them a mail questionnaire regarding their customer satisfaction survey procedures and their use of survey results. We also requested copies of their survey instruments, which we analyzed for content and format. We received 72 completed questionnaires and 63 survey instruments.

FINDINGS

Virtually All Risk and Cost HMOs Conduct Customer Satisfaction Surveys

All but one of our respondent HMOs (99 percent) conduct general customer satisfaction surveys.

However, Most HMOs Do Not Target Their Medicare Members

More than half of the HMOs (55 percent) have never conducted a customer satisfaction survey of their Medicare members only. Furthermore, almost all of these (97 percent) also do not include questions specific to Medicare members on their general surveys. More than one-third of all HMOs (39 percent) do not know the satisfaction rate of their Medicare members for their last general survey, and most (65 percent) do not know the Medicare response rate. However, the Medicare specific data which is available shows that Medicare members have high satisfaction rates.

HMO Customer Satisfaction Survey Instruments and Procedures Lack Uniformity

The satisfaction survey instruments used by HMOs vary widely in their format and content; in fact, no two are the same. These instruments differ in their comprehensiveness and in the rating scales and satisfaction questions used. The survey procedures HMOs use also vary. This lack of uniformity in HMO surveys renders comparisons between HMOs difficult, if not impossible, when assessing Medicare beneficiaries' satisfaction with their plans.

While in Many Ways Basically Sound, Technical Weaknesses in Many HMO Surveys May Mask Problems and Inflate Satisfaction With Managed Care Plans

Many HMOs appear to be following sound survey principles regarding sampling and increasing response rates. Most are also using survey instruments containing clearly worded and focused questions (98 percent) and covering a broad range of satisfaction dimensions (71 percent.) However, many HMO survey instruments do contain weaknesses which may bias, to some degree, survey results. Most significantly, more than half (58 percent) include no questions about problems with or complaints about health plan services, and twenty-nine percent use survey instruments which include an unbalanced five-point rating scale of three positive, one neutral and only one negative response category. Most HMOs are also lacking mail follow-up procedures (21 of 32 which use mail surveys) and are not conducting non-respondent analyses (87 percent.) One-third of HMOs scored adequate on an index of instrument adequacy, and less than half (44 percent) scored adequate on an index of procedure adequacy.

HMOs Use Their Survey Results as Much for Marketing as for Quality Improvement

Nearly three-fourths of HMOs (74 percent) say they use the results of their customer satisfaction surveys to market themselves to potential new members. A similar number (76 percent) report also using their customer satisfaction data to develop quality improvement or corrective action plans. A majority of HMOs share their survey findings with physicians (76 percent) and with plan members (67 percent.)

IMPLICATIONS FOR MEDICARE

We believe the usefulness of customer satisfaction surveys as currently conducted by HMOs is substantially reduced by their lack of uniformity, limited focus on Medicare beneficiaries and technical weaknesses. Therefore, if HCFA seeks data on the satisfaction of Medicare beneficiaries with managed care, we believe it can not rely upon industry surveys as they are now conducted. The HCFA may want to consider alternative approaches to measuring Medicare client satisfaction with managed care, such as conducting its own surveys or requiring HMOs to periodically survey their Medicare members with a standardized instrument and comparable procedures.

The Office of Inspector General is planning further work surveying Medicare beneficiaries about their experiences with HMOs. We will once again conduct a survey of Medicare HMO members similar to one already completed. We are also working on a technical assistance report which will provide HCFA with a more detailed discussion of our methodology for conducting beneficiary surveys and will identify useful survey techniques and methods based on our prior experience.

COMMENTS

We received favorable comments from HCFA on the draft report, expressing their appreciation for the timeliness and significance of our study. In particular, HCFA states that this report will be a major factor in influencing its decision to develop its own beneficiary satisfaction survey capability. The actual comments received are included in Appendix C.

INTRODUCTION

PURPOSE

To assess how Medicare health maintenance organizations (HMOs) are conducting customer satisfaction surveys and how they are utilizing the results of these surveys.

BACKGROUND

In various staff meetings, the Office of Managed Care in the Health Care Financing Administration (HCFA) asked the Office of Inspector General (OIG) to survey how Medicare HMOs are measuring customer satisfaction and using the resulting data. The OIG was asked to pay particular attention to what the managed care industry is doing to measure the satisfaction of its Medicare members. The HCFA requested this study in order to better ascertain how active its role should be in surveying Medicare HMO enrollees and how the surveys HMOs are conducting can be of use to HCFA in its monitoring efforts.

This report follows earlier OIG reports on Medicare managed care. These included one entitled "Beneficiary Perspectives of Medicare Risk HMOs" which surveyed beneficiaries about their experiences with HMOs. This report found that while risk HMOs provide adequate service access for most of their Medicare enrollees, some serious problems remained with enrollment procedures and service access and disenrollees were more likely than enrollees to have experienced problems with HMO services. A further report on "Medicare Risk HMOs: Beneficiary Enrollment and Service Access Problems" looked more closely at HMO-level data to identify the distribution of these problems and found that they existed in varying degrees of intensity among HMOs and more frequently with disenrollees than with enrollees. Another report, entitled "Medicare Risk HMO Performance Indicators," found that HMO disenrollment rates, along with customer satisfaction surveys, appear to be useful managed care performance indicators.

The Industry

Health maintenance organizations are a form of managed care in which a patient selects a primary care physician from a group of approved plan providers to act as the patient's first point of contact within the health care system. This physician must authorize any specialist, hospital or other type of care the patient receives. According to industry estimates, approximately 50 million individuals in the United States are enrolled in one of the 550 HMOs across the country.

An HMO can pay its physicians in different ways. A primary care physician or specialist can be paid on a capitation basis, in which he or she is paid one monthly amount per each patient regardless of how much care that patient receives. Physicians can also be paid on a fee-for-service basis. Some HMOs use a combination of these different payment methods.

Medicare HMOs

Medicare beneficiaries have the option of receiving their health care from an HMO approved by HCFA. Once approved, the HMO generally applies for a risk or cost Medicare contract. In a risk contract, the HMO provides the full Medicare benefit package and is paid on a prospective per capita basis, in which it is required to absorb any financial losses but is permitted to retain any financial savings. Under such a contract, payment is made on a prepaid capitation basis with no retroactive adjustment. The HCFA encourages HMOs to apply for risk contracts. In a cost contract, the HMO also provides the full Medicare benefit package but is paid on a reasonable cost basis. An HMO can also serve Medicare patients through a health care prepayment plan agreement or as a demonstration project.

The number of Medicare risk and cost contracts continues to grow. As of February 1, 1995, 157 plans had risk contracts and 30 had cost contracts with HCFA, with a total enrollment of approximately 2.5 Medicare million beneficiaries. This is an increase from July of last year, when there were 136 risk HMOs and 27 cost HMOs. In February 1993, only 87 HMOs had risk contracts to serve Medicare beneficiaries.

While only about seven percent of the Medicare population nationwide is enrolled in HMOs, the geographical distribution of this enrollment varies widely. The distribution of Medicare HMO enrollees is concentrated in four States: California, New York, Florida, and Arizona. A few States have no Medicare beneficiaries enrolled in managed care programs.

Section 42 CFR 417.107(h) of the regulations require federally qualified HMOs with Medicare enrollees to implement ongoing quality assurance programs. These programs must have the following basic components: a quality assurance methodology, a peer review process, systematic data collection of performance and patient results, and remedial action procedures.

As part of the systematic data collection requirement listed above, HMOs are required to share their data collection results with their providers of care and institute any needed changes based on these results. Data can be collected from any of several different sources, including member satisfaction surveys. These surveys, however, are not required by law.

Customer Satisfaction Initiatives

Several efforts have been under way in the managed care industry to develop methodologies and instruments for measuring and reporting performance ratings, including customer satisfaction, in managed health care. These initiatives have primarily been motivated by an interest in the industry and among health care consumers in establishing standard measures by both individuals and employers can compare and contrast different health plans. Few of these initiatives, however, are specifically aimed at the Medicare population.

Two industry groups are particularly active in managed care quality and customer satisfaction issues. The National Committee for Quality Assurance (NCQA) is a voluntary private accreditation agency active in setting and enforcing HMO quality standards. In November 1993, it developed the Health Plan Employer Data and Information Set (HEDIS), which defines performance measures to evaluate, among other things, a plan's quality of care, member access to care, and member satisfaction. The NCQA publishes the results of its accreditation reviews nationwide. Also, the Group Health Association of America (GHAA), a managed care industry group to which most HMOs belong, has developed a model consumer satisfaction questionnaire which is available to its members.

METHODOLOGY

In conducting this inspection, we selected a stratified random sample out of the universe of 185 HMO risk and cost contracts with Medicare beneficiaries enrolled as of February 1, 1995 (nine additional HMO risk and cost contracts were dropped from the universe because they had no Medicare enrollees at the time the sample was drawn.) These HMO contracts were stratified into three groups of high, medium and low Medicare enrollment, based on the number of Medicare beneficiaries in each. The HMOs in the high stratum have Medicare enrollments of larger than 42,550, while those in the medium and low strata have between 42,500 and 1000 and less than 1000 Medicare members respectively. We purposely contacted all of the contracts in the high stratum. See Appendix A for a more detailed explanation of strata selection.

We selected 95 HMO risk and cost contracts for the final sample: all 13 from the first stratum, 70 from the second stratum, and 12 from the third stratum. Medicare enrollment in the 13 high stratum contracts accounts for 51 percent of all Medicare enrollment nationwide in managed care. Forty-seven different HMOs across the country hold these 95 contracts. Eighty-two of the 95 are risk contracts, and the remaining 13 are cost contracts.

We sent all 95 a mail questionnaire which requested information about their customer satisfaction survey procedures and their use of survey results. We also requested copies of the HMOs' survey instruments. After allowing six weeks for data collection, during which time we conducted a second mailing to non-respondents, we achieved an overall response rate of 76 percent for the questionnaires. We also achieved a 66 percent overall response rate for the survey instruments after making a minimum of two follow-up telephone calls to HMOs who did not initially send us their instruments. For the mail questionnaires, we achieved response rates of 100 percent for the high stratum, 77 percent for the medium stratum, and 42 percent for the low stratum. For the survey instruments, we achieved response rates of 100, 64 and 42 percent for each of the three strata respectively. All differences reported between strata are statistically significant at the 95 percent confidence level.

Differing response rates among strata suggest the possibility of non-response bias. While we did use Chi-square to test for such bias, due to our relatively small sample size and resulting small cell sizes in the two-variable tables, it was not a valid test. Therefore, we acknowledge the possibility of non-response bias but are not able to quantify it.

To assess HMO customer satisfaction survey procedures, we reviewed the returned mail questionnaires to determine, among other things, their sampling methods, follow-up procedures, and their means of determining response and satisfaction rates. Our findings on survey procedures are based on the HMOs' answers to these questionnaires. See Appendix A for confidence intervals of fifteen key questions.

To assess HMO survey instruments, we developed a detailed review sheet which we used to systematically evaluate each instrument for both form and content. This review sheet included assessments of each instrument's length, dimensions of satisfaction measured, scales and format used, clarity of instructions and questions, and user friendliness.

We also constructed two indexes of survey adequacy - one for instruments and the other for procedures. We used data from the instrument review sheets discussed above to construct the index of instrument adequacy. This index was based on three key variables: comprehensiveness of satisfaction dimensions, balanced response categories, and problem specific questions. The index of procedure adequacy was based on four variables: level of confidence sought, frequency of follow-up efforts, conducting a non-respondent analysis, and use of balanced criteria for determining overall satisfaction. For these four variables, we used indicators from the questionnaires returned by HMOs. In each of the two indexes, we gave the variables a subscore, which were then combined to give total scores for instrument adequacy and procedure adequacy respectively. The indexes of survey adequacy are explained in greater detail in Appendix B.

This inspection was conducted in accordance with the **Quality Standards for Inspections** issued by the President's Council on Integrity and Efficiency.

FINDINGS

VIRTUALLY ALL RISK AND COST HMOs CONDUCT CUSTOMER SATISFACTION SURVEYS

General Membership Satisfaction Surveys

All but one of the respondent HMOs (99 percent) conduct general customer satisfaction surveys. Almost all (95 percent) consider these general surveys to be very or somewhat useful. A majority of HMOs (60 percent) conduct their surveys at least once a year, while thirteen percent survey their members twice a year. Most of the remaining 28 percent conduct satisfaction surveys on an ongoing basis.

Nearly three-fourths of HMOs occasionally (24 percent) or always (49 percent) use a professional research agency to conduct their customer satisfaction surveys, with a total of 37 different research firms cited by the responding HMOs. All of the HMOs with high Medicare enrollment hire professional research firms, as compared to 70 percent of HMOs with medium and low Medicare enrollments.

Other Types of Surveys

A majority of HMOs are also conducting other types of surveys. These include surveys of disenrollees (92 percent), on the functional or health status of their members (58 percent), and of the working aged (53 percent.) Fifty-nine percent of HMOs also survey the physicians who work for them about their satisfaction.

HOWEVER, MOST HMOs DO NOT TARGET THEIR MEDICARE MEMBERS

Medicare Satisfaction Surveys

While HMOs conduct satisfaction surveys of their general memberships, they pay less specific attention to their Medicare members. More than half of the HMOs (54 percent) have never conducted a customer satisfaction survey of their Medicare members only; in fact, eight percent of these survey only their commercial, non-Medicare, members on satisfaction. Seven of the HMOs who have not yet conducted a Medicare only survey did volunteer, however, that they are planning to do so within the next year. Almost all of the HMOs (97 percent) which do not conduct Medicare only surveys also do not include questions specific to Medicare members on their general surveys; the few who do ask only a limited number of Medicare questions.

While most HMOs have the potential to identify Medicare members in their general surveys by identifying the respondent's age, for the most part they are not extracting Medicare specific data. More than one-third of all HMOs (39 percent) do not know the satisfaction rate of their Medicare members for their last general survey, and most (65 percent) do not know the Medicare response rate. Nevertheless, whether or not they survey Medicare enrollees, more than half of the HMOs (58 percent) believe it is easier to survey Medicare members than it is to survey non-Medicare members, primarily because the former are more responsive, have more time, and are easier to reach.

The Medicare data which is available shows that Medicare HMO members have high satisfaction rates. All of the HMOs with Medicare data report overall satisfaction rates of 75 percent or higher for their Medicare members. Similarly, virtually all (99 percent) report the same 75 percent or higher satisfaction rate for all members.

HMO CUSTOMER SATISFACTION SURVEY INSTRUMENTS AND PROCEDURES LACK UNIFORMITY

The lack of uniformity in HMO survey instruments and procedures renders comparisons between HMOs difficult, if not impossible, when assessing Medicare beneficiaries' satisfaction with their plans.

Satisfaction Survey Instruments

The survey instruments used by HMOs vary widely in their format and content. No two risk and cost HMOs use the same instrument. Of our sample survey instruments, none use an exact duplication of the GHAA satisfaction survey instrument, although almost half (48 percent) use some exact or similar headings, questions and rating scales from that survey. The HMO instruments differ significantly in their length, ranging in size from 1 to 45 pages and including from between 9 to 159 different questions.

Rating scales and overall satisfaction questions on survey instruments are also inconsistent across HMOs. Our review of HMOs' instruments identified 26 different scales used for responses, ranging from a simple two-point scale of yes or no, to a ten-point scale covering a range of satisfaction levels. Fourteen different types of questions are used to measure overall satisfaction, including questions which ask about satisfaction with medical care, most recent visit, quality of service, health plan and a particular medical center. Three-fourths of HMOs, however, use a question about satisfaction with their plan to measure overall satisfaction.

Satisfaction Survey Procedures

Sampling procedures also differ. Fourteen percent of HMOs survey their entire membership. Of the 86 percent who survey a sample of their membership, sample sizes vary from 100 to over 5000. The size and type of sample used varies according to the purpose of each HMO's survey. While most (51 percent) use a simple random sample, another 41 percent use a stratified random sample, and eight percent a purposive sample. Forty-nine percent of the HMOs select their sample from a universe of one particular subgroup, as defined, for example, by a minimum length of membership, while most of the remaining sample from the universe of their entire membership.

Furthermore, other survey procedures used by HMOs vary. Forty-four percent administer their customer satisfaction survey by telephone only, 16 percent administer it by telephone and mail, and 37 percent by mail only. The remaining generally use an in-office self-administered questionnaire in combination with mail or telephone. Excluding those which conduct ongoing surveys, sixty-two percent of HMOs stop data collection after ten weeks and the remaining third continue collecting data for longer than ten weeks.

WHILE IN MANY WAYS BASICALLY SOUND, TECHNICAL WEAKNESSES IN MANY HMO SURVEYS MAY MASK PROBLEMS AND INFLATE SATISFACTION WITH MANAGED CARE PLANS

HMO Survey Strengths

Many HMOs appear to be following sound survey principles regarding sampling, efforts to increase response rates by telephone, and instrumentation. A majority (71 percent) were seeking confidence intervals of 95 percent or higher in designing their sample size. Close to half (44 percent) used sample sizes of over 1000 members, which, in combination with their generally high response rates, should have ensured a good level of precision in their surveys. Additionally, most HMOs who use telephone surveys make a strong effort to maximize their response rates. Almost all of these (94 percent) try to contact members at least three times before considering them to be non-respondents.

Furthermore, our review of HMO survey instruments revealed several positive features. A great majority of the instruments generally include questions which are specific (92 percent), clearly worded (98 percent) and focused on only one thought at a time (98 percent.) The instruments also cover a broad range of satisfaction dimensions. The most common include ability to provide prompt service (96 percent), overall satisfaction with services (87 percent), staff courtesy (84 percent), access to services (82 percent), physician communication (81 percent), and physician competence (77 percent.) Of the seventeen possible dimensions of satisfaction we looked for in the HMOs' instruments, a majority (71 percent) include at least ten.

HMO Survey Instrument Weaknesses

However, our instrument review also revealed some weaknesses in the survey instruments which may bias, to some degree, survey results. More than half of the instruments (58 percent) include no questions about problems with or complaints about health plan services. Of the 42 percent which do include these topics, most ask only one or two questions. For the most part, the questionnaires ask only if a member has ever had a problem with or complaint about their care, and how satisfied he or she was with its resolution. The OIG report referenced earlier on beneficiary perspectives of risk HMOs included several questions in its beneficiary survey specific to problems with HMO services. These questions were important in understanding, among other things, reasons for dissatisfaction and disenrollment with HMOs. Half of the instruments (51 percent) do not ask respondents for their suggestions for improving the HMO.

Other deficiencies noted in the HMOs' instruments may compromise their objectivity. Forty-six percent use at least one unbalanced rating scale. The most common of these, a five-point rating scale of three positive, one neutral and only one negative response category, is used by twenty-nine percent of the HMOs. Furthermore, of the quarter which use agree or disagree statements, almost all include only positive statements for respondents to respond to. While this has the advantage of ensuring greater ease for the respondent, it also has the disadvantage of possibly resulting in more positive ratings. Other weaknesses noted include few or unclear interviewer instructions on telephone survey instruments (24 percent), confusing or unclear questionnaire formats (20 percent), and inconsistent rating scales (20 percent) and repetitive questions within an instrument (15 percent.)

We also rated each survey instrument to determine its level of user friendliness. In doing this, we looked for several qualities, including clarity of format, simplicity of directions and questions, and overall attractiveness. While most surveys (73 percent) were rated user friendly, only eleven percent were rated very user friendly and 16 percent were deemed not user friendly. A majority (80 percent) of those rated user friendly are mail surveys, while most (70 percent) rated not user friendly for either the respondent or the interviewer are telephone surveys.

HMO Survey Procedure Weaknesses

Most HMOs are also lacking certain survey procedures which, if used, may increase survey accuracy. Twenty-nine of 32 sample HMOs which use mail surveys do not try to contact members who do not return their original questionnaires; just one-third send non-respondents a second copy. Additionally, a large majority (87 percent) have never conducted a non-respondent analysis, which would enable them to know if non-respondents differed in any way from respondents, thus alerting them to possible bias in the survey findings. Finally, less than half of the HMOs (43 percent) have ever conducted a bilingual survey. All of these HMOs have conducted surveys in Spanish, and many are based in States with a large Spanish-speaking population. The lack of a bilingual survey may be a survey weakness in those geographical areas with large numbers of non-English speaking clients; without them, the experiences and satisfaction of these clients can not be fully comprehended.

Indexes of Survey Adequacy

As described in our methodology and explained in Appendix B, we constructed two indexes of survey adequacy - one for instruments and the other for procedures. One-third of the HMOs' instruments (32 percent) scored adequate on our survey instrument index, while another 28 percent scored somewhat adequate. Of the remaining instruments, 24 percent scored somewhat inadequate and 16 percent inadequate.

The HMOs were also scored on the adequacy of their survey procedures. On this index, less than one-half (44 percent) scored adequate, and thirty-one percent scored somewhat adequate. Another ten percent of the HMOs scored somewhat inadequate, while 15 percent scored inadequate.

HMOs USE THEIR SURVEY RESULTS AS MUCH FOR MARKETING AS FOR QUALITY IMPROVEMENT

Marketing

A majority of HMOs are using their satisfaction surveys in their marketing plans. Nearly three-fourths (74 percent) say they use the results of their customer satisfaction surveys to attract potential new members. Most of this marketing consists of reporting survey data in speeches or other oral presentations, and in pamphlets or brochures. Seventeen percent use their survey findings for advertising purposes. The HMOs which use their survey results for marketing have higher overall satisfaction rates than those which do not market their survey results; 46 percent of the former report overall satisfaction rates of 75 percent or more, while 20 percent of the latter report the same overall satisfaction rates.

Quality Improvement

A similar number of HMOs utilize survey results for quality improvement purposes. Three-fourths (76 percent) report using their customer satisfaction data to develop improvement or corrective action plans. One-third (34 percent) use the results for tracking performance and developing strategic goals. Almost all (97 percent) include their satisfaction surveys in their Medicare quality assurance programs.

Most HMOs also share their survey results with employees and members. A majority distribute their survey findings to physicians (76 percent) and to plan customers (67 percent.) In fact, more than one-third (36 percent) use these results to determine all or part of their physician reimbursement. Of those HMOs who conduct satisfaction surveys of their physicians, a few (16 percent) compare these results to those of their member satisfaction survey results.

Differences Between HMOs

The HMOs use their survey results somewhat differently depending on the size of their Medicare enrollment. Almost all of the HMOs with high Medicare enrollment (92 percent) use their survey data for quality improvement purposes, compared to 75 percent of HMOs with medium and low Medicare enrollments. Marketing of survey results is conducted by 58 percent of high enrollment HMOs, in contrast to 75 percent of medium and low enrollment HMOs. A comparison of the instruments used by high Medicare enrollment HMOs with those used by medium and low Medicare enrollment HMOs reveals some important differences in this regard. For example, more than half of the former (69 percent) have questions which ask members about problems or complaints with their health plans, as compared to just forty percent of the latter. Also, HMOs with a large number of Medicare enrollees are more likely to ask for suggestions for improvement on their questionnaires than are HMOs with fewer Medicare enrollees.

IMPLICATIONS FOR MEDICARE

We believe the usefulness of customer satisfaction surveys as currently conducted by HMOs is substantially reduced by their lack of uniformity, limited focus on Medicare beneficiaries and technical weaknesses. Therefore, if HCFA seeks data on the satisfaction of Medicare beneficiaries with managed care, we believe it can not rely upon industry surveys as they are now conducted. The HCFA may want to consider alternative approaches to measuring Medicare client satisfaction with managed care, such as conducting its own surveys or requiring HMOs to periodically survey their Medicare members with a standardized instrument and comparable procedures.

The Office of Inspector General is planning further work surveying Medicare beneficiaries about their experiences with HMOs. We will once again conduct a survey of Medicare HMO members similar to one already completed. We are also working on a technical assistance report which will provide HCFA with a more detailed discussion of our methodology for conducting beneficiary surveys and will identify useful survey techniques and methods based on our prior experience.

COMMENTS

We received favorable comments from HCFA on the draft report, expressing their appreciation for the timeliness and significance of our study. In particular, HCFA states that this report will be a major factor in influencing its decision to develop its own beneficiary satisfaction survey capability. The actual comments received are included in Appendix C.